Adjusting to Brain Inju

This important book in the *After Brain Injury: Survivor Stories Series* tells the story of four people who suffered acquired brain injuries: Karl Hargreaves and Ashraf Sheikh as a result of road traffic accidents, Lisa Summerill because of a stroke and Meg Archer as a result of meningitis.

Each person tells their story in their own words, describing what happened to them, how they dealt with it and how they experienced the recovery process. The cases represent very different types of people and severity of injury but are alike in providing raw accounts of the challenges faced whilst also highlighting their resilience and determination to carve out new lives. Alongside these inspirational stories are contributions by friends and family, as well as several members of the interdisciplinary rehabilitation team to give a broader view of the whole process of recovery. By combining expert commentary with real-life experiences, this book points towards sources of support, normalises the experience and provides a context for understanding the challenges and successes in each case.

This book provides support, understanding and hope for patients who have suffered a brain injury. It is valuable reading for any professional involved in neurorehabilitation and students of clinical neuropsychology.

Dr Katherine Dawson is a clinical neuropsychologist and treats patients in various rehabilitation settings with a range of neurological conditions, including traumatic brain injury, stroke, spinal cord injury and brain infections. Katherine has interest in cognitive rehabilitation and works with individuals and family to manage emotional and behavioural changes following acquired brain injury. Katherine is currently involved in research with the NHS regarding telerehabilitation and acquired brain injury.

After Brain Injury: Survivor Stories

This new series of books is aimed at those who have suffered a brain injury, and their families and carers. Each book focuses on a different condition, such as face blindness, amnesia and neglect, or diagnosis, such as encephalitis and locked-in syndrome, resulting from brain injury. Readers will learn about life before the brain injury, the early days of diagnosis, the effects of the brain injury, the process of rehabilitation and life now. Alongside this personal perspective, professional commentary is also provided by a specialist in neuropsychological rehabilitation, making the books relevant for professionals working in rehabilitation such as psychologists, speech and language therapists, occupational therapists, social workers and rehabilitation doctors. They will also appeal to clinical psychology trainees and undergraduate and graduate students in neuropsychology, rehabilitation science and related courses who value the case study approach.

With this series, we also hope to help expand awareness of brain injury and its consequences. The World Health Organisation has recently acknowledged the need to raise the profile of mental health issues (with the WHO Mental Health Action Plan 2013-20), and we believe there needs to be a similar focus on psychological, neurological and behavioural issues caused by brain disorder and a deeper understanding of the importance of rehabilitation support. Giving a voice to these survivors of brain injury is a step in the right direction.

Series Editor: Barbara A. Wilson
Published titles:

Life After a Rare Brain Tumour and Supplementary Motor Area Syndrome
Awake Behind Closed Eyes
Alex Jelly, Adel Helmy, Barbara A. Wilson

Life and Suicide Following Brain Injury
A Personal and Professional Account
Alyson Norman

Adjusting to Brain Injury
Reflections from Survivors, Family Members and Clinicians
Katherine Dawson with Karl Hargreaves, Ashraf Sheikh, Lisa Summerill and Meg Archer

For more information about this series, please visit: https://www.routledge.com/After-Brain-Injury-Survivor-Stories/book-series/ABI

Adjusting to Brain Injury

Reflections from Survivors, Family Members and Clinicians

Katherine Dawson with
Karl Hargreaves, Ashraf Sheikh,
Lisa Summerill and Meg Archer

Routledge
Taylor & Francis Group
LONDON AND NEW YORK

First published 2021
by Routledge
2 Park Square, Milton Park, Abingdon, Oxon OX14 4RN

and by Routledge
52 Vanderbilt Avenue, New York, NY 10017

Routledge is an imprint of the Taylor & Francis Group, an informa business

British Library Cataloguing-in-Publication Data
A catalogue record for this book is available from the British Library

Library of Congress Cataloging-in-Publication Data

A catalog record has been requested for this book

ISBN: 9780367629304 (hbk)
ISBN: 9780367629298 (pbk)
ISBN: 9781003111481 (ebk)

Typeset in Times New Roman
by KnowledgeWorks Global Ltd.

Contents

Acknowledgements

To all my clients I work with; your experiences have shaped this book and my practise: I have learnt such a great deal and continue to do so. Huge thanks to Chris Lomas for recording these stories and his commitment in completing the book. Also, a very big thank you to Mike Oddy for reading the manuscript and writing the foreword (and for also being a fantastic supervisor). Finally, I am very grateful to my family for their ongoing support and enthusiasm (and a very special thank you to my mum).

Donations

Karl, Ash, Lisa, Meg and I have decided to donate our proportion of sales of the book to the following charities:

- SameYou
- Headway – the brain injury association
- Meningitis Now
- Paul For Brain Recovery
- Different Strokes

Foreword

Michael Oddy

The process of adjusting to a brain injury is never easy; not for the family and especially not for the individual concerned. As this book shows no two people are the same, no two brains are the same, and the rehabilitation required is never exactly the same. This makes it difficult to help those new to brain injury to understand what they have been through, what they are currently going through and where they must go next.

This book is aimed at the person with the brain injury, but it could be equally valuable for relatives and professionals as well. For the latter it reminds us that their inner strength is frequently retained by the person with the injury. Indeed, this strength is often increased as people find greater reserves within them.

This book reminds us of the paradox that brain injury changes people, yet it doesn't change people. There is almost always still part of the original person shining through. The four people contributing to this book certainly shine through. Karl's confidence returns as he battles to salvage a life after brain injury. Ash shows that he has never lost his desire or ability to help and support others. Lisa finds ways to create a new normal and maintain strong relationships with her husband and her family, in spite of the changes she has experienced. Meg emerges from the natural despair she experienced when waking from her illness to find that, at such an early stage in her life, so much had changed. Despite this she was subsequently able to develop a new life and a philosophy that enables her to see the positives in her life.

The book is unusual in that it allows all the individuals concerned to speak with their own voice. Co-ordinated by Dr Katherine Dawson, an experienced clinical neuropsychologist, the book allows the professional members of the team to explain how they work, adapting their approach to the particular needs of the person and the family they are working with. Family members also describe their role in supporting their loved one and the process they have gone through in understanding the changes in that person, learning to accept these changes and finding ways to develop a new, different, but equally important and rewarding relationship with the individual. In some cases, this may be a younger member of the family taking on the role of a carer or supporter having being cared for and supported by that same individual in the past.

The fact that all the important actors are given a voice means that this book will be of value to those who find themselves in a similar position. The book gains credibility by having the individual and his or her family member contribute their thoughts and views.

It takes courage to talk as openly as Karl, Ash, Lisa and Meg have done in this book. This is especially so when one is feeling vulnerable. All four have done so because they have a desire to help others who find themselves in the same situation. To lay bare such vulnerabilities is not something any of us would do lightly, and the writers of this book deserve huge credit for doing so for the benefit of others who will follow them. As others read through this book, many of the points described by the four main contributors will resonate strongly with them. The book will merit reading and re-reading as they go further on the journey. Points that did not resonate will do so. Reading the reflections of the professionals may also help the individual to understand more about their brain injury and their rehabilitation. The success achieved by the four writers will inspire those who follow them. This in turn may help them achieve a more positive mood and to participate more vigorously in their rehabilitation. Adopting a new persona and leaving behind an old persona is the theme of this book. This is hard to achieve but essential to do if one is to walk confidently into the future.

Michael Oddy, January 2020

Introduction

Katherine Dawson

Karl, Ash, Lisa and Meg – the other main contributors to this book – all have one life-altering and shattering experience in common. They have each suffered acquired brain injuries. This book is their account of how they and their families dealt with this, and the rehabilitation that led to their making new lives. As their neuropsychologist, I was part of the team who worked with them on their rehab.

Writing this book was (sort of) Karl's idea. As Karl was beginning to adjust to his injury, he asked me if I could recommend anything written by someone who had suffered a brain injury like his. I tentatively suggested Karl told his story. He said he would but only if I agreed to be a co-author. The idea grew to include Ash, Lisa and Meg's experiences also. We then thought it would be helpful to add the voices of some of the other rehab team members so that you could find out more about the whole rehab process from different points of view.

I wanted to focus on identity following brain injury because a strong theme of the work I do with individuals involves a very significant struggle to make sense of who they are following injury. Whilst the concept of hidden disability is regularly talked about, a lot of my clients find this one of the biggest challenges. Changes in thinking, memory and, for example, the ability to keep a lid on your emotions and behaviour, whilst hidden, can have a major impact on all sorts of areas of someone's life. Sometimes, the behaviour is the bit that is seen, without the context of these very real challenges that individuals face. I also wanted to write about the fact that as time from injury increases, and individuals return home and try and return to their previous roles, the hidden difficulties are often more disabling than any physical disability and the need to focus on meaningful community rehab is crucial.

My passion for the importance of neuro-rehab stems in part from growing up with my sister who has Down's syndrome. She is now 37-years-old and lives a very full and meaningful life. She has worked as a learning support assistant in a special needs school, she is very musical (she plays the piano and lives to sing and dance), she enjoys regular physical exercise and she is a much-loved Aunty. I have been fortunate to grow up realising that what my sister can do far outweighs what she cannot do. The emphasis on individual strengths and meaningful roles is therefore a big part of why I enjoy working in the field of community-based neuro rehab.

I remember reading about social disability following brain injury. I was sold on the concept that by scaffolding their environment differently – tapping into an individual's strengths and reducing some of the stressors around the person – significant and meaningful changes could be made to someone's life after injury. It also ties into the concept that after trauma, individuals naturally move towards a place of adjustment and whilst there are certainly challenges along the way, we see a great deal of resilience organically emerge during rehab.

Working in this field has also made me realise the importance of team working (which Dr Salawu talks about in more detail in the following section). Our overall team aim when we begin rehab is putting in place 'optimum' rehab conditions. I talk more about this in Karl's story, but this includes healthy brain routines and habits around sleep, fatigue management and pacing, physical exercise, nutrition and the provision of tools to cope with emerging anxiety and low mood. Early on, we are also breaking down meaningful activities (which fit with an individual's values) as these are crucial in order to engage and motivate our clients. Each team member plays critical roles, but we all work in the same direction, with coordination being a core part of the case manager's role. The role of the rehab assistant/support worker is also key. I work in teams with fantastic support workers who come with such enthusiasm and creativity, and in specific cases, I have observed the vehicle of change being the longer term relationship that is developed.

As rehab starts, it is really important to have a good understanding of a client's initial strengths and weaknesses (both physically and in terms of thinking, memory and emotions). Our work then focuses on putting a supportive framework around the individual, with the aim of reducing current demands. I spend a lot of time with individuals and families discussing the resource-demand model. Basically, after an injury, the demands an individual are under significantly outweigh their resources, and we need to work together with the individual to balance out the scales so they feel more able to cope. Rehab should start by ensuring individuals experience some success in the meaningful activities that are programmed into their rehab timetable. Experiencing success early on in rehab strengthens motivation. Critically, how we engage an individual should be thought about, taking into account what is important to someone, their strengths and weaknesses. The more creative the approach is, the better it is. In the teams I work into, there is a lot of time spent thinking outside the box... Sam Smith songs, butchers sausages, power chills and Minion memes have all played a part in previous rehab plans. As rehab progresses, we then increase the demand and pace gradually as this supports the concept of neuroplasticity; with challenges and new activities, the brain can rewire and develop new connections.

When is the right time to engage in rehab? Dr Salawu talks about this in more detail. But in terms of providing education about brain injury and establishing routines, and the importance of a rehab plan – I agree that the sooner, the better. However, at the same time, I believe that as one of my clients (G) said to me recently 'reaching a goal is an ongoing process and not a one-time event.' Therefore, whatever stage someone is at in their journey, there is always something that can be done to reduce barriers and facilitate work with family and individuals to support recovery.

Everyone involved in writing this book hope it will answer some questions for those who have had a brain injury. We also wanted to illustrate what can be achieved with the help of good community rehab and a supportive family. All of our contributors have spoken very openly and honestly about their key relationships, and, I think you will gain a great deal from their very honest assessments of the ups and downs of life since their injury or illness.

In Part Two, you will hear from Karl, who talks about the ways in which his life was torn apart after a road traffic accident, and explore his rehab journey with real candour. But first, in Part One, Dr Salawu will explain a little bit more about the early stages of treatment and referral and explore goal setting and 'prehabilitation...'

Part I

Early-stage treatment and referral

Abayomi Salawu

Introduction

Essentially, my job is to help people get back – as much as possible – to the level of functioning they had before their illness or injury. Unfortunately, there is no curative treatment for the majority of the patients I see. Just as there is no cure for a patient with multiple sclerosis, there is no 'cure' for somebody who has had a stroke. Their treatment will focus on rehabilitating them and getting them back to their previous level of functioning, while helping to reduce the risk of a subsequent stroke.

In other countries, they call this work physical medicine, or physiatry in America. It is a very broad spectrum of disciplines, including the following:

- Neuro rehabilitation, dealing with the brain and memory
- Musculoskeletal rehabilitation, dealing with physical injuries
- Amputee rehabilitation for people who have lost a limb
- Cardiac and respiratory rehabilitation
- Sports medicine

Getting people back to full function requires a multidisciplinary approach. So we work as part of a team, alongside our colleagues in physiotherapy, occupational therapy, speech and language therapy, as well as with dieticians, and psychologists.

That is because when somebody has had a stroke or a head injury, they will not just have a physical deficit, there will be psychological ramifications too. In assessing whether they will be able to get back to their previous level of functioning we need to ask:

Will they be able to get back to work?
Are they able to reintegrate with family life?
What support will they need when they leave hospital?

In some cases, the psychological burden they're under can make their physical deficit worse. It is a bit like having a wound; after the accident or illness, there will be a scar. And we call that a residual deficit. The size of 'the scar' determines how much it affects their life from that point on. So, a big part of what we do is working to eliminate the impact of that residual deficit/that scar.

Some of our work comes under the heading of adaptation. Patients will exhibit adaptive behaviours anyway; sometimes if their left side is injured or weakened as a result of an accident or a stroke, they will naturally start to favour their right side. And we will look at compensatory behaviours to help them to adapt while still trying to move them back towards their previous level of function.

Early intervention isn't early enough!

The earlier rehab can begin, the better. I always say, it is even more effective if you start on rehab before you get your injury or have your illness! I know that sounds counterintuitive – how can you start on therapy before you have an accident? But now, more and more people are talking about this theory of 'prehabilitation...'

You can see how the concept of prehabilitation is gaining traction in cancer care, for example. So before they have surgery, patients are encouraged to start on the exercises they will need to do post-operatively. I did some similar work in a research programme a few years ago, working with patients with brain tumours. We know that being physically active is a key part in helping people to stay healthy. So in my study, I looked at the effects of exercise and tried to establish how well people would be able to tolerate chemotherapy and radiotherapy. The results showed that the fitter you can make the patients, the more they can tolerate the process. So we're keen to promote prehab as a general concept – the fitter you are, the better you will be able to engage in rehab, and treatment.

In every case, we try to encourage patients to get back to some form of movement as quickly as they possibly can. Let's say that a patient has broken a limb. Part of their treatment is to rest that limb – not to rest the whole body! The limbs that are not broken should all be kept active.

If you lie in bed for a week, you lose between twelve and forty per cent of your muscle mass! Three weeks in bed is equivalent – in terms of physiological parameters – to forty years of aging. The good news is that you will start to recover as soon as you get more active, and we're here to encourage you to get moving!

Setting patient goals

After I have spent time assessing a patient, I will recommend the different pathways they will need to follow. Then each practitioner will carry out their own assessment and set their goals for the patient. Together, we can then agree the primary goals that we will focus on.

We work to a system of SMART goals. That is to say that every goal should be

- Specific
- Measurable
- Achievable
- Realistic
- Time resourced

There is no point in setting goals that aren't achievable. So if somebody comes in with a severe head injury and tells me they want to be able to run the London marathon, we have to acknowledge that it might not be an achievable goal. We have to break it down into bite size targets. That might start with something as basic as being able to stand unaided, and walk a little way.

It is great to hear a patient express big ambitions – and we need to harness their desire – but we have to be pragmatic and work within what each person can realistically achieve. Motivation is key, and if a person struggles by taking on too much, too soon, it can be deeply demotivating.

The rehab process is split into the inpatient phase and the community phase. Many people worry that when they leave hospital, they will be left to their own devices. But it is rare that patients will have made enough progress at the point of discharge to go back to the lives they led before. We believe that it's when patients are discharged that the work really begins, and we will give them the targets and goals that they will need to work towards.

The value of recovery in a community setting

We always have to be flexible. Some patients will carry out the work they need to do better in the community than they would in rehab. I am keen that patients should be hospitalised for as short a time as possible so they can return to some form of normality. It is very important to do as much rehab in the real world as possible.

We carry out a routine patient assessment before we discharge anyone. For example, we test that people are able to carry out – as far as possible – the sorts of routine tasks they will need to do at home. We take people to the road within the hospital grounds to see if they could manage crossing a road unaided. While this is a useful test, we have to bear in mind that the test conditions don't replicate real life. There is a 10 – 20 mph speed limit within the grounds, and most drivers proceed with extra caution. So, while it is still valuable to see what patients will do, and how they will cope with their new reality, nothing beats the real world experience.

This is an example of the specificity of training. For example, if you want to be a fast bowler in cricket, you practise all the elements you need to master, the run up, the acceleration and the delivery. Similarly, if I want someone to negotiate the roads around their home, we need to take them walking there as often as possible. And that's why community rehabilitation is so vital.

The value of multi-disciplinary teams

Very few aspects of patient rehab are unifactoral; there are many different elements to a patient's impairment. To give you another example from the world of sport, most people do their training and then compete in their chosen sport. But some people achieve more. Often that is because they take extra factors into account. They work with sports psychologists, nutritionists and trainers, and it's the same with helping people recover.

We tend to think of the body as composed of lots of separate parts, but that is a little bit misleading. In our work, it helps to take a view of the body as a whole and consider the different elements that contribute to helping people improve their functional deficit. So a patient who has a mobility impairment; this is not just purely a physical issue, there might be psychological, environmental and behavioural factors in addition to the neurological factors at play.

Neuroplasticity

We used to think that after the age of about four years old, your brain was effectively set. But now we know that is not true. We know that the brain continues to change throughout life, like any living tissue.

Without wanting to oversimplify too much, if we had to describe the three main functions of the brain, we would say that it helps us to

- Think
- Feel
- Move

Of these three things, the only one we can really control is the movement. You can direct the thinking, but you can't switch it on or off. You can direct the feeling, but you can't switch it on or off. But you can decide when and how to move. The moment I think about typing these words, my fingers move and help me do it. So the currency of the brain lies in the movement.

It is believed that thought processes also have a movement correlate. The extraordinary thing is that, if the brain uses a particular pathway to do a function, the surrounding nerves in the area near the damaged pathway have the potential to take over that function if they are asked.

The key question is how do we ask those other nerves to carry out those functions?

I should point out that this doesn't happen for everybody. Sadly, it doesn't happen for most people. But for those in whom it does happen, there can be a considerable restoration of lost function.

When we work with head injury or stroke patients, we do a scan showing which parts of the brain have been damaged. Then we repeat the scan further down the treatment pathway. What we usually see is that, even though some of the lost function has returned, that part of the brain is still damaged. So this shows how other parts of the brain have effectively taken over. That's neuroplasticity in a nutshell.

Whether or not this will work in individual cases comes down to many factors. For example, we know that up to 40% of people who have had a stroke may suffer from low mood and depression, and depression can also affect the rehabilitative process and recovery. So if you don't address the depression, they won't be able to engage in their rehab therapy. This emphasises the importance of a multi-disciplinary approach.

Another important element in a successful rehab process is the power law of repetition. In other words, if you want to get good at something, you need to practise it, for example 10^4 or ten thousand times. Now, if you try to practise something with a paralysed limb, the limb will not respond. It can't. For many people, the normal response at this point is to give up. Never mind ten thousand, these people won't even make it to ten attempts! That is the biggest obstacle for many people, but this is where, potentially, technology can be used.

I have a special interest in rehabilitative technology, and there is more useful equipment coming onto the market now that tries to augment brain plasticity by motivating practice and repetition of tasks. Some of this equipment works on the brainwaves so that when the patient thinks about the movement, we can use that brainwave to power an app connected to a computer. This allows them to see an image of a virtual arm that will actually do what they are thinking.

This technology works on the basis that the biggest motivator for doing anything is success. If you try something and it works, you're motivated to do it again, and to go on doing it. So this technology is a great way to encourage people to keep practising.

There are many exciting avenues of research, and we are learning more all the time.

Good luck on your journey

Over the course of this book you will read about many different kinds of patient experience, with a particular emphasis on the work people have done in the community. Every person who has contributed to this book has experienced good and bad times. But I think they have all made astonishing progress. Most of all, they all give me hope – and I hope they give you hope – that progress is always possible.

Part II

Fractured

Katherine Dawson

Introduction

It was never going to work. It was a waste of his time and mine...

That summed up Karl's expectations of the work we were going to do together. We met in April 2016. It was just about a year after Karl had suffered a dreadful road traffic accident.

If you have had a brain injury – or you know someone who has – it is going to feel overwhelming at times. And Karl was sceptical that anything we could do would make any material difference to his life. But fast forward to the summer of 2018 and Karl had a different, more positive take on it. He told me that the experience was like 'having someone get into my head and find stuff I never even knew was there – and then helping me to understand what's going on.'

For family and carers

If you are going to be caring for someone who has had a brain injury, I believe early intervention from a rehab team is key.

There is so much that can be done in the early stages of recovery to really boost a person's level of independence and well-being, as well as their physical ability and function. This is a critical stage that can make a profound difference to the quality of people's lives. So it's very important that we're all pulling in the same direction.

The sooner you can understand about the sorts of behaviours someone might present with – and the link with their brain injury – the better. Otherwise, you might find that you miss certain attributes, or put certain behaviours down to the person not paying attention, being lazy and disinterested, being rude or outspoken, or choosing to overlook their own difficulties. Sometimes families say "he/she was always like this," and I often wonder whether this is a way of coping in the face of the trauma that everyone has been through. However, the earlier you can understand the brain, and the hidden disabilities that people have to live with (rather than just the difficulties you can see) the more receptive you'll be to supporting someone.

Don't forget – *you'll* need emotional support too. We talk a lot about the ways in which the patient's experience can be a lot like a bereavement – we went through that process with Karl. And it can feel like a bereavement for you too. So, make sure you have support. Find someone you can talk to about your experience, and look after yourself. You can't pour from an empty cup. In other words, there's only so much support you can give if there's nothing left in your own reserves. It's really important (for both of you) that you have time set aside just for you. I know how hard it can be to balance that with all the practical demands on your time, as well as the potential guilt about not being available every minute of the day. But it is so important, and I hope this book will help you to find the right balance.

For clients

In this section of the book, I want to talk you through the process I follow and hopefully offer some reassurance. Not everyone will follow exactly the same techniques as I do, but the principles are the same.

Along the way, I'll try and answer some of the most common questions people ask me about what's involved in rehab.

My involvement

I work in two different areas. Firstly, I work a lot with case managers and rehab teams, in cases where, due to the nature of the accidents, the funding comes from insurance companies. And I'll tell you a bit more about the way that works when I discuss some of the work I did with Karl in more detail.

Secondly, our team has now begun offering community rehabilitation to individuals who either self-refer or have been referred to us by the NHS. That is because many people don't have access to funds for rehab, as was the case in Ash's and Lisa's stories, as you'll see.

We feel strongly that timely and focussed bursts of rehab can really progress someone's independence and support individuals back to more meaningful roles in life. We work with some fantastic rehab assistants to do this work in the NHS, and one of our rehab assistants, Tim, talks more about this a little later on.

What does a neuropsychologist do?

A neuropsychologist works with individuals who have been diagnosed with some form of acquired brain injury or neurological condition. We are specifically concerned with the link between what has happened in someone's brain and any changes in thinking and memory, emotions and behaviour.

We often conduct neuropsychological assessments, which involves completing a set of questions or tests that specifically look at different brain functions such as memory, attention, language and perception. The results help to work out individuals' strengths and weaknesses, which we then use to inform our rehab approach. We also look at mood, and how this is impacting upon activity levels, social life and networks.

We spend time with family and any care staff too, as the more information we can build up about what is going on, the more able we will be to help. This information allows us to prescribe a bespoke intervention plan, which we'll carry out in close conjunction with any other members of the team.

What happens first?

Before I get involved, a case manager is assigned to the patient to oversee the whole treatment process. This will be somebody with a good awareness of brain injury and rehab, who will understand when to pull different professionals into the process. They will coordinate all necessary meetings, and above all, they'll build up a good relationship with the patient to help them navigate the next few months or years of the work that we'll do together.

In Karl's case, I was brought on board along with an occupational therapist and a neurological physiotherapist, as he had needs in all those areas. A support worker may sometimes get involved too, helping the patient in establishing new routines and habits and reducing some of the demands that a patient has in their life. This relationship can work really well in certain cases.

The work we do is carefully coordinated, and everyone involved meets regularly to ensure that we're all pulling in the same direction to meet the client's goals as far as possible. Sometimes that means collaborating on joint strategies, for example, I might join forces with the physiotherapist if the client is too anxious to engage in aspects of physical therapy. This collaborative work helps make the whole process feel more meaningful. In Karl's case, the physio came up with the idea of starting rock climbing with Karl, and this had a massive impact on his self-esteem, and at the same time, it was great cognitive rehab to help with his planning and attention. This is a good example of how working together as a team helped stretch Karl's capabilities both physically and psychologically.

As part of my referral from the case manager, I'll get information about when the person was injured, and the severity of the injury. I'll get access to any assessment reports that have been done, with recommendations from the case manager. I'll also find out about people's acute recovery – that includes which hospitals they've been in. This will all help me understand some of the effects, and the likely impact of the accident.

The brain scan reports take me a stage further, and the description of the injury will give me more insight into the likely effects. (Karl mentioned how we were able to understand why he was getting dizzy spells at Headley Court, and that was because we could see the damage to his cerebellum – the part of the brain that coordinates movement – on his scans.)

The work that I do isn't just with the patients themselves. I expect to do a lot of work with their families too, so it's useful for me to find out more about their background and family history. The more I know, the easier it is to build the right kind of recovery plan. And you'll see why this was such an important part in directing Karl's recovery.

It's time to meet the client…

Chapter 1

Karl's story

Karl Hargreaves

Whenever I tell my story, I'm tempted to start on that day, and on that road, where I was pronounced dead. With the woman who fell asleep at the wheel and ploughed into my motorbike. The woman who nearly killed me.

But maybe this time, I'll do it differently.

Part of me *did* die that day. The man I am today is not the man I was. But, after working with Katherine, maybe it's time to tell this story in a different way.

Because this story really starts with two unlikely people falling in love…

My dad was from Accrington, but my mum was from Madrid. She came over to stay with some of her family in England and was working in a psychiatric hospital near Blackburn. My dad was working there as a painter and decorator at the time – and that's where they met.

It wasn't an obvious match. For a start, she couldn't speak much English. But my dad had a bet with his mates… Apparently, loads of people had tried asking my mum out and had all got nowhere, so they challenged him, and the rest is history.

They got married and settled in Blackburn. Dad joined the RAF shortly after I was born. Growing up in the forces, you get used to moving around. By the time my brother,

Vince, came along, Dad was at RAF Marham, and then, with us two scaly brats in tow – it's what the Air Force calls kids – Mum and Dad moved to Gibraltar, and then onto RAF Athan in South Wales. It felt like we never stayed in any one place too long. And most of my childhood memories are all fractured – little bits of playing on the beach on Gibraltar and camping in dens in the middle of the Welsh countryside.

I do remember the first time I kissed a girl. I must have been about ten. It's funny how that memory has stayed with me, even after I've lost so many others!

I went to boarding school at Lancaster Royal Grammar and did well in my O-Levels. I stayed on to do my A-Levels, although I didn't do so well, because, by then, I was exploring other interests! I seem to remember spending most of my time smoking and getting drunk… I had fun. It was a good time. But I didn't know what to do next…

I ended up doing the classic thing of working at McDonalds for a few months, until I got fired for taking a burger out of the waste food bin and eating it! And that was the start of my chequered employment history…

I got a job at a petrol station and lasted three days! I stacked shelves on the night shift at Morrisons for a bit. Then there was a job at JJB Sports, which lasted about six months. After that, I worked as a postman. It meant a six-day working week, and early starts, but it left the evenings free. That was when I started DJ'ing with a friend who DJ'd in a nightclub, and it grew from there. Some nights we'd drive up to Stockport. And on Sunday nights we went all the way to Kirkcaldy in Scotland, then drive back to start work at 5.15 on a Monday morning. I was knackered by Monday afternoon.

I enjoyed the creative freedom I got from DJ'ing, but I was starting to feel restless at work. Maybe it was the life of constant motion I'd lived growing up, or maybe, I was finally starting to realise I needed a bigger challenge in my working life. I'd been coasting since my O-Levels, and maybe, I was finally ready to take on something a bit more demanding...

My daughter was born on Valentine's Day 1994, and that gave me a more demanding job to explore! But I was still looking for the next big work challenge. After about eighteen months with the Post Office, I took a job with a hydraulics company. I worked on the trade counter where people challenged us to fix things, and we made all sorts of pipe networks and hoses and components for cherry pickers and cranes. I hadn't done any engineering-type work before, I'd never done anything like with it my dad – he was an RAF cook – but I had an aptitude for it, and I loved it.

I might even have stayed there for years, but it was a competitive market and times were tough. Their profits were getting squeezed tight. They had to make somebody redundant, and it had to be me. Last one in, first one out. But that job changed something in me – I had finally found something that I really enjoyed, so that's when I applied to join the RAF as an engineer.

I was twenty-six when I joined the RAF, and I loved it all...

Being a bit older helped me find my feet quickly. A lot of the other guys were fresh out of school and a bit wet behind the ears. But I'd had quite an active life, and I knew the ropes from my days as a scaly brat. So I already had an idea of what to expect and how to take it when you're being ordered around! I knew that you had to show respect to your superiors – that came naturally to me – but it was hard work for a lot of the younger guys.

I did seven weeks' basic training at RAF Halton, followed by a year of trade training at RAF Cosford. I passed out from there as a Leading Aircraftman, and husband… Yes, somehow, I managed to find the time to fall in love and get married!

We went as a couple to my posting at RAF St Athan, and I was assigned to 'crash and smash' – where we recovered aircraft that were unable to fly and transported them back in pieces.

Eighteen months later, we were back at Cosford for more trade training. It's not an easy life for a forces wife. I was used to the constant upheaval of moving around, but it's hard when you're not used to it. I remember my wife saying, "If you get posted back to St Athan again after this, I will leave you!" She'd had to leave Cosford once already, and she didn't want to have to face that same upheaval again.

But… I'd enjoyed the crash and smash so much that I applied for the job again in secret and got it. Predictably, going back to crash and smash meant our relationship crashed and burned. I can't even remember how long we were together – but it must have been about two and a half to three years. In the end, I think it was quite amicable. But it's hard to remember now…

I do know that I learnt something about myself during that time. Perhaps it should have been obvious, given my track record, but the simple truth was – I got bored of things, people and places very quickly. That's why being in the RAF, moving from camp to camp, and job to job, was so perfect for me. But not for her. If being an RAF wife is a strange life, being a crash and smash wife is even stranger. I would be expected to spend about three out of every four weeks away, working on other camps. And that brings its own pressures. And its own temptations.

A lot of the time I was working away, I was enjoying myself a little too much, even though I was married. And in the end, maybe that's why the marriage really broke down. I came to terms with the fact I was bored of it; we weren't happy. So, we got divorced while I was in South Wales. I had a few different partners during that time, but I met my second wife while I was on a job near Kings Lynn, and – to cut a short story shorter – we got married on a whim. Registry office, tee shirt, two witnesses and then down to the pub.

After that, we were posted to South Wales for a bit. I got promoted to Corporal and posted back to RAF Cosford as an instructor. I taught a component of the course that I did as part of my mechanic training, and I really enjoyed it. I loved showing people how it all worked and got a real sense of satisfaction out of seeing them learn something new. It made me feel great; I loved every second of it. But out of the classroom? The same sense of boredom had come over me. I had started seeing other people, and I knew the writing was on the wall. Another marriage was over.

After the dust had settled, I got a detachment to the Falklands for four months, and that's when I met Amy…

AMY: Karl had already been out in the Falklands for a couple of months when I was posted there in March 2010. He seemed pretty crazy when I met him for this first time – his hair was even crazier than it is now. You're not supposed to be that crazy in the RAF, but he got away with it!

We both liked getting out and about and seeing the wildlife. Karl's a really good photographer, and he was always keen to get other people involved.

I was only in the Falklands for a couple of months and left a week or so before Karl to go back to Brize Norton. We'd built up a good relationship in those two months, so we stayed in touch after we got back.

We had a great time together, so when I was promoted to Sergeant and posted down to RAF Brize Norton, working on Hercules aircraft, we hooked up again. She bought a house in Carterton in the autumn of 2012, next to the camp, and I moved out of the senior accommodation block and went to live with her.

We lived there for six or seven months. It was going well. But as always, things changed...

A new job came up, leading a mechanics course on one of our aircrafts, but it meant spending a year in America. True to form, I thought, *that sounds like fun! These kinds of opportunities don't grow on trees!* So of course, I applied, and I got it. The question of what moving away for a year was going to do to our relationship hardly entered my mind. But Amy didn't begrudge me my chance.

AMY: There wasn't any discussion about Karl going to America. I knew he was fiercely independent, so when he decided to go, he did it. He said "I've seen a job advertised... it's in America." And that was it. He wanted it; he went for it. That was Karl. We parted as friends.

I was posted to the Offutt Air Force Base in Omaha, Nebraska. Working with the US Air Force engineers, I learned every detail about that aircraft so that I could go home to England and generate a course so we wouldn't have to send people to America to learn about the aircraft.

It was the same old story. I worked hard, and I partied hard. And inevitably, I knew that it wasn't fair to

Amy to keep any kind of relationship going. We broke up officially while I was out there, but then, when I came back, just before Christmas 2014, we lived together, as friends for a few months. Amy was lovely about it. She never resented me. Even after we split up, it never felt acrimonious… although I never thought I'd see much of her ever again.

The truth is my career was everything to me. I loved my life, and I loved my work. It was a job that never let me get bored. I enjoyed every new opportunity that came my way. I felt invincible.

AMY: We were still friends. I sent Karl a text on his birthday, but didn't hear anything for weeks. And then, one sunny day in May, I got a knock at the door…

*

I'd started seeing a girl called Angela, who lives up near York…

We met near the cathedral and had a drink at the pub… I know the name, but I've forgotten it…

I remember driving up to her house – and the plastic panels on the floor of the TT kept getting snagged under my feet, so I took them off…

I know we went to an Audi Volkswagen show, and we had great fun doing that…

Was it before or after Christmas…? I don't remember… There's just a massive chunk missing, there's nothing to anchor my memories on, before and after that day…

The 13th of May 2015.

I was on the A17, coming back from Boston. Everything I know (or think I know) has come from what other people have told me. My own memories just aren't there anymore.

I've seen the photographs… it was a bright, sunny day, and I was riding on a proper, straight road. All the witnesses said that I was riding in a professional manner, only doing around 50-mph on a 60-mph road.

It should never have happened. Later, the police told me that she – the driver of the car – had flown back from France to Heathrow, then driven from Heathrow to Sleaford for a couple of hours, before driving back to Norfolk. She was 68 years old, and she just fell asleep at the wheel. Her car drifted into the other lane; she hit a truck on my side of the road and then tore straight into me, head-on.

I saw the photographs of my bike, in little pieces, spread out as far as the eye could see, all over the road and scattered out across the field. The headstock was broken off. Even the break discs were buckled – and those things don't bend.

I can look at all the photos – of the bike in pieces – and still not remember a thing about it.

I was just so lucky; there was a guy in a nearby car – a fellow biker – called Andy Hull, and he came straight over. My feet were over my head somewhere, I wasn't breathing, and he thought: *this guy's dead.* And I was actually clinically dead at that point. My heart had stopped. It was all over for me. Andy was going to go over and try to help some of the other people in the accident, but something stopped him, he took a closer look at me and decided in a flash to try CPR. He did not want to give up on me. He said he had to punch me so hard to get my heart beating, but my ribs were already broken anyway. I've got him to thank for saving my life.

When the air ambulance arrived to scrape me off the road, they told Andy they didn't expect me to be alive by the time they got me back to hospital…

AMY: It had been a really sunny day, and I remember looking out of the window and thinking, Karl will be out on his bike today. I'd got back to camp after working a funny shift, and that's when I heard the knock at the door. I opened it to an RAF colleague who told me Karl had been involved in an accident. (It turns out that I was still listed as Karl's emergency point of contact on the computer at work.) My colleague told me we needed to get to the Queens Medical Centre in Nottingham as soon as possible.

I didn't know if Karl was dead or alive, or how bad his injuries might be. I didn't even have time to think about how strange it was that, months after we'd split up, I was still Karl's emergency contact, and I was the one that was going to be by his bedside.

We got to the hospital first, but Karl's sister, Rebecca, was just a couple of minutes behind us. They let her in to verify that it was Karl, but the rest of us had to wait outside. His dad, his step-mum and his brother arrived too.

He wasn't conscious. They'd put him in an induced coma because they didn't know if there was any damage to the brain. Considering what I know now, he didn't look that bad, but he was hooked up to all sorts of machines. They said that he'd broken both his legs and damaged a lung. But apart from all the wires, he just looked like someone asleep in bed with a couple of cuts and bruises.

The next day, they put a bolt in his head to relieve the pressure on his brain, and they put some cages on his legs to keep them in place. There wasn't much else they could do; they just needed to make sure he was more settled before he could be moved to another hospital.

At that time, we still didn't know exactly what had happened. No one ever came and told us, and it was 2 days later when Karl's brother managed to find out from the police.

Over those first few days, I'd talk to Karl over and over. He was still unconscious – who knows if he could hear me – but I wanted him to know he wasn't alone. I wasn't worried that he'd find it strange to see me there, but I was worried about what sort of state he'd be in when he woke up. Nobody knew. They couldn't tell what his responses would be; there was no way to predict just how bad the damage was.

I went back and visited Karl every day for the first two weeks. I still felt like I needed to be there for him. He got on with his family, but after all the time we'd shared over the last few years, I felt as if I knew Karl better than most. I felt like I had to be there to help him. I never considered not going to the hospital to see him.

It was five days until he started to come round. At first, he just opened his eyes and stared through you, like you weren't there. He was out of intensive care, but still in major trauma, and they got the physio in every day, to try and get him into a sitting position. He didn't seem to know what was happening at that time, but they needed to keep the blood flowing properly.

Eventually, the medical team managed to get him to say "Hello," to his dad, but he didn't really seem very aware of what was going on.

When he was lying in the bed, his legs would move uncontrollably, almost as if he was trying to crawl out of bed. I could put his music on to help him calm down, and he seemed to listen, but he was still staring right through me.

*

After a couple of weeks, they moved him to the Queen Elizabeth Hospital in Birmingham. The first time I saw him there, I was able to feed him a bit of a banana custard desert, although a lot of it dribbled back out. He still couldn't really speak at that stage. But the time after that, things had changed a lot. They'd had him sitting up in a wheelchair with his neck held in place, and he looked at me as I came in and said simply "Hello." There was some recognition there, but he still didn't know quite who I was – whether I was his girlfriend or his wife. But he took my hand and held it to his cheek.

I tried to get to Birmingham at least once a week, and his friends from work made sure they went in as often as they could. About four weeks on from the accident, little signs of improvement started coming in stages. He seemed very happy after he started recognising people again.

There were plenty of dips along the way. I took my mum to see him, and all he could do that day was throw himself around the bed and swear a lot. He obviously wanted something very badly; he just couldn't tell us what. So he just kept on swearing, and it was making all the other families around us more and more uncomfortable.

He could get quite angry too. Especially with the nurses. He didn't really like them doing anything, and some of them complained about him. When he wasn't happy about something he'd get right up in your face, and really shout at you. When that happened, I just had to leave, go and get a coffee and let him work thorough the anger. Then, when I got back, he wouldn't have remembered the shouting. He wouldn't even have remembered that I'd been there a few minutes earlier.

But I knew that wasn't the real Karl – I imagined that was a common thing to happen to someone who'd had such a bad brain injury.

I didn't find it hard being there for him, even though we'd split up. The hardest part was knowing that I couldn't ever do as much as I wanted to because I was ill at the time too. Our families are quite different – I'm very close to my family, and I think that if it had been me in Karl's position, they would have been there every day. So I found it quite hard thinking that Karl didn't have someone with him all the time. That's nothing against Karl's family; it's just the way he is. He's always been so independent.

*

My first fragments of memories returning were from Birmingham – and they're some of the most traumatic bits…

I remember having an enema a couple of times – that was not fun – and then shitting my bed, because I couldn't move. I couldn't walk or anything. I still feel sorry for the nurses; they don't get paid enough having to deal with that mess.

I remember Amy helping me to the toilet and complaining that I couldn't defecate. I was so desperate that I had my finger shoved up my arse, trying to help it out because it was that bad.

It wasn't only the crash I couldn't remember – so much of my life was just – missing. When my family came in to visit me, I wanted to know where mum was… They actually had to remind me that my mum had died a few years ago. I had totally forgotten. Even though I had known she was gone, and even though I'd been at her funeral, it was like hearing the news for the first time – it was heart-breaking.

Dealing with my family was really hard. They were all treating me as if everything was as normal as you could expect, under the circumstances. But it wasn't like that for me. All those relationships just didn't exist in the same way in my mind. Some of them weren't there at all. It was as if they had been erased. When my own daughter came to see me, I told her to sod off! I had no idea who she was.

My inhibitions were gone too. I was swearing a lot; I was definitely rude to my daughter – although I can't remember any of that now, either. I know my brother and sister came in to see me, but I can't picture it; I can only really remember Amy being there for me.

What do you do when someone turns up at your door and tells you your **ex**-boyfriend's at death's door? Amy's such a lovely person; she didn't just come to see me that one time, she kept coming back. I didn't know it then, but she spent hours with me, just watching over me, making sure I was alright.

And I really needed her there for me...

AMY: I'd bought him a mobile phone, I thought it would help keep him connected with the outside world. I tried to show him how to use it, but of course, he wanted to work it all out for himself. Then, one night, I noticed a couple of missed calls from him, and when he phoned again, and I picked up, he was frantic. He said, "They're trying to kill me. The nurses want to kill me. Phone the police... I need help!"

My brain was totally fuddled. I remember dialling 999 that night and telling them *they* were out to get me. I was terrified, and I was shitting myself. When I told them where I was, the operator said to me "Can't you get one of the staff onto the phone?" and I told her, "I can't – they're all in on it!"

Afterwards, I rang Amy, and she told me that, whenever I felt stressed, I had to look at the photos of my family and friends on the wall, and that would help me to remember who I was and remind me that I was safe. Amy helped bring me down and keep me calm.

But while Amy was helping me – the woman the nurses assumed was my wife – Angela – came to see me. Their paths crossed a couple of times, and I know it was a bit strange because neither of them really knew who the other one was. The hospital staff were confused by it too. I'm just glad I can't remember any of that!

AMY: There were problems about my status at the hospital. The only word Karl could use to describe me was 'wife.' So everyone was very confused. Eventually, I have to tell him that we weren't together anymore, and he teared up. It was strange, especially compared with the time when we'd separated. I'd gone out to see him that Christmas when he was in America, and he was just Karl being Karl. He was absolutely blasé about separating then. But this time, it was different. He couldn't even remember splitting up with me. In his mind, it had been his sister that had gone out to visit him in America!

*

Eventually I got into a wheelchair, and I remember going out for some fresh air with a couple of mates from work. It was weeks later. My memories were still in tatters, but I had to start work on my physical recovery too. I got some basic bits of Lego to try, but I was annoyed because I couldn't put them together. My dexterity and coordination were awful. It's still bad now, compared with what it used to be like, but it was terrible then. And it was so frustrating!

In August – about 3 months after the crash – I was taken to the Defence Military Rehabilitation Centre at Headley Court in Surrey…

AMY: He was just so excited. It was like Christmas! He was looking forward to getting his hair cut at 5 o'clock, and every few minutes, he asked, "What time is it now? I'm having my hair cut at five." Then he wanted me to pack his bags for him because "If you don't do it for me, who will?"

He was **so** excited about it all – until he got there!

He went from being in a room with other people – opposite to the nurse's station, so they could watch him, in case he tried to get out of his bed – into a room on his own, in a place he didn't know.

I worried for him at weekends, when he didn't have a structured programme. It was difficult to think that he was there on his own, with nothing to do. I tried to get there as much as I could. The first weekend I went there, Karl's sister visited too with her children, and we took Karl out in his wheelchair. But the next time I went down and stayed a few weeks later, Karl was suddenly walking around with his sticks. He could even make me a cup of tea again. And he could hold a conversation. I'd gone from seeing him every day, to every week, to once a month, so the changes were so obvious. Not all of the changes were so positive though…

There were signs that his personality had changed a lot. Karl had started to see things in very black and white terms. If something angered him – and it could be the stupidest thing – he got really furious. If a child was running around in a shop and stepped in front of him, Karl would just stand there and glare. He wouldn't think: I should move aside; he'd think: they're in my way, why should I move? Or if we were looking at something on a shelf, and I tried to move him because someone was trying to get past, he wouldn't do it. "No! Why should I move out of the way?" And that was a big change. He used to have a lot more patience; the change in him was clear to see.

He was still piecing things together bit by bit. One time, someone came to visit and mentioned that Cilla Black had died. Karl looked at me as if he was going to cry. I don't think he understood if that was a person he knew; someone he should be upset about. So I had to explain that Cilla Black had been on TV – and it wasn't someone he had ever known.

There were some positive personality shifts too. Before the crash, Karl had been fiercely independent. He had always done exactly what he wanted to do, but during his recovery, there was a more accommodating side to him. He was suddenly quite happy to do things that maybe he wasn't so interested in doing.

It wasn't long before he began to reject anything boring though, and slowly, he started to seem a bit more like the old Karl, particularly when he started to rely more on technology, and his tablet again.

*

Headley Court *was* boring. I appreciate what they did for me, but I wasn't happy there. It was all set up to help victims of war and conflict survivors. I was in the category of people who needed help, but I wasn't a war survivor; it wasn't quite right for me. And I didn't know how I was supposed to try and be independent with so many people around doing things for me. At least they let me go home for Christmas!

AMY: They gave him a month off – a therapy break – and he came to my parent's house for Christmas. After that, he went back to Headley Court for another month – and that's when they put him through his driving tests. But that was tough for him. That was around the time his dizziness started.

When I went back in the new year, I started to have feelings of dizziness really badly. As soon as I saw Katherine and Nicola (my community rehab physio), they looked at the brain scans and figured it out straightaway. It was a side effect of all the damage to my cerebellum. My eyesight had been affected too. The horizontals were fine, but the verticals were skewwhiff on my sight test. It's not surprising my balance was off.

When I'd arrived at Headley Court, they'd made me hand my licence in; they said it would be easier to get it back at the end. So long as I didn't feel too dizzy, I did the driving. I still feel the frustration of not being instinctively as good as I was before. But I passed enough of the DVLA tests to get my licence back, and I was very happy about that.

Angela came to rescue me from Headley Court at the end of January and took me back to York with her. But it just didn't work. I still had no idea who she was – not really. We both struggled with it, of course. We had been building something and then suddenly, it was all taken away from us. Our whole relationship – everything it was and everything it could have been – was taken away from us. When she looked at me, she saw the person I had been, and the memories we had made together. But when I looked at her, I saw next-to-nothing.

I was due back at work a couple of weeks later, and Angela drove me back to RAF Waddington. That's when I had to tell her, "I can't do this anymore." It wasn't her fault, and it wasn't mine. It was all because of that nutter in the car who ran me over! My memory was still in tatters, and I had no idea what the hell I was doing, where I was, or even who I was. I knew I had to concentrate on getting myself right before I could progress with a relationship, so I had to call it a day.

I had to simplify my relationship with Amy too. We were still mates, and maybe that was part of the problem. The man I was becoming needed to see things in black and white, not shades of grey. My relationship with Amy was more 'between the lines,' and I just couldn't cope with that ambiguity. So I bagged all of her stuff up, and left it ready for her, so that if she ever needed to stay with me, she could. But only on the understanding that it was a visit, and all that stuff would need to be put away again afterwards. Leaving it lying around wasn't the closed door, black and white picture of our relationship that I needed then. We both needed that clarification and that closure.

In a way, she'd become like a sister, and I had no complaints about that, but it wasn't what you want in a romantic relationship. Perhaps that was a bit of the old Karl coming out – I suddenly felt as if my future was all mapped out with Amy, and I didn't want that. I wanted to enjoy the uncertainty again – the sense of not knowing what's coming next. That's what helped keep me going.

There were lots of times when we had fun together, but a lot of the time, perhaps because of a past we'd had (that I just couldn't remember) or because she was a continuous vein, running all the way through my recovery, she left me feeling tethered to the pain of the past. I found that I was getting angry with her really easily, and I didn't like it. It wasn't fair to her after everything she'd done for me. But I felt as if I couldn't help it. I could see how upset it made her, of course. Then it would upset me too – and that only exacerbated it.

That anger threatened to overwhelm me – and it wasn't just about the crash – it affected everything. There were stages – for a long time afterwards when I was very,

very angry. And there were times when I didn't think I would ever be able to get past the anger.

I'd always been a very short-tempered, minimal-patience person anyway, but afterwards, it was all exaggerated, and it would escalate so quickly when something set me off.

At first, I wasn't even aware of the signals that I was getting annoyed. But, in time, and with Katherine's help, I learned to read the signals when I was 'moving into the red,' and I've got more control over it now than I used to have. I know what to do to bring myself back down to a calmer state.

AMY: When Karl exploded with anger, Katherine gave us different colours to help – red, green and blue. One time when I spilt some coffee on his leg, he shouted "I am red!" and stormed out of the room. So that was a positive change – rather than just shouting and railing at me, he knew he had to get out.

That's when he started to recognise when he was doing something that wasn't normal and was able to do something about it. I can't remember him ever having that anger in him before the accident. (And I'm the one who can make him angry most of the time!)

*

I went back to work part time to start with – just three hours a week. It was tough going, and I soon learned how much I'd been looked after outside of work. Despite everything that had happened, the Air Force kept faith in me. On paper, I should have been discharged straightaway, but when they saw how much progress I'd made, they wanted to give me another chance.

I'd already created the course I'd been asked to devise before the accident, and someone else was brought in to teach it based on my work. I went back for a few hours each week to work alongside him and refine the course. And we started work on a second course, specifically for managers. I just had to try and take it slowly.

The information that I needed was mostly still in my head, and sometimes little things triggered memories of other things that I'd totally forgotten even existed. Or I'd see something, and it'd bring it all back to me. The hope was that I'd be able to work my way back to working full-time...

But I realised I wasn't cut out to be in the Air Force anymore. I just couldn't do it. I'd been going in for one or two hours a week and feeling destroyed at the end of it. There was no way I could manage being an aircraft technician, never mind a military aircraft technician. So, we all discussed it, and we all agreed; I was officially released in November 2018.

I never wanted to leave, of course. I wanted to go on working. But I just couldn't do it. After all of the time I'd spent imagining myself getting back to work, I came to accept that it wasn't going to happen. It wasn't a shock in the end. There had been such a gradual process – from realising how much had changed for me while I was still in hospital, to going through rehab, to trying to go back to work and not being able to do it. Eventually I got used to the idea of not being able to go back to work.

*

I didn't have any clear ideas of what I wanted to do with the rest of my life when I left the RAF, and one year later, I still don't.

Life is very different, and I'm still coming to terms with that. The desire to go back to work hasn't gone. I still wish I could go back – it's not just the work I miss, it's the whole package, the social side of it too. I miss that. But I've tried, and I can't.

The biggest issue for me now isn't the physical injuries; it's the mental issues. Any time I have to concentrate for a while, I get knackered. It's my mind that feels the fatigue. So, I don't think too far ahead, I just try to take each day as it comes.

Perhaps the hardest thing to come to terms with has been knowing that, in a sense, I did die. The old Karl – everything I was – died on that road. My memories, my experiences, even my skills and abilities… I lost so much. And I had to learn to let go and move on. I didn't have any other choice. But it was like starting from scratch.

Waking up to that new life was like being a newborn, except I'd been born in a grown-up's body. I didn't just have to learn to walk again; I had to learn how to do *everything* again.

I've just taught myself how to bake again. I've taught myself how to use my synthesisers again, I've taught myself how to make videos – but it was tough. There was neuro work, physio and all sorts of rehab too. And it all took time. A lot of time.

Socially, things are different now I've left work. I can't go out to the pub or go out with my mates anymore because I don't have the confidence or the ability – and because I'm absolutely knackered all the time. So I tend to stay in, tinkering with the car, creating fractals on the computer, listening to music and doing lots of baking.

I feel as if I've got to a stage where I have stopped relying on other people. It felt as if my brain was tapping me on the shoulder, saying, "Look, it's time to jump onto your own train tracks of life, and crack on, rather than relying on other people for stuff." And I do feel like I'm at that point now where I can manage. It's not easy. Of course it's not. But I've always been a very independent person, and I finally feel like I've got a bit of that back again – it's a little glimpse of the old Karl. There were still elements of me buried away inside, I just had to find them again.

Katherine was a huge help. And I had to eat my own words a little bit, because when we met, I told her flat out, "I understand what you do, but you can't help me. There's nothing you can do for me!" But it's turned out that the neuropsychological help has been the bedrock of my whole recovery, taking my brain into places I didn't even know existed. Getting stuff out of me that I never even knew was there. It's uncovered so much – I've been able to notice issues that I never knew existed before. I hate the word 'strategies,' but I've been able to adopt strategies to cope with these issues, manage them better and move on.

*

I'm glad I'm still friends with Amy, and I know we'll always be an important part of each other's lives. I'll never not be friends with her. She's been that much of a help for me since going through the accident. There's no way I could take her out of my life again. It's that big a deal.

AMY: Looks like I can't get rid of him!

But I don't think we'd have been like this if he hadn't had his accident. We'd probably have just drifted apart. We drive each other up the wall sometimes… But I've seen what he's been through, so when he does erupt over something, I know to ignore it. It can be something stupid like cutting a pizza and not cutting it properly. So while I'm sawing away at it, Karl is getting more and more angry and ends up stabbing the counter – and I have to tell him to go and cool down. One night, I came in and closed the curtains because it was dark outside, and it turned out that, according to Karl, that was the wrong thing to do...

*

Sometimes I have to laugh when some of these things are told back to me later. And I think, I'm bloody mental!

I do get angry sometimes, but like I've said to Amy, it's never personal. I just can't help it. And then that frustrates me because then I can see that even though I don't mean to, I'm upsetting someone else.

Amy's been awesome – and a pain in the arse as well – but I wouldn't change any of it – I needed it. She gave me a good kick up the backside when I deserved it.

Eighteen months later...

It's eighteen months after I wrote my story – four and a half years since the accident – and my life looks completely different. I still like to be busy, and my time is always filled. I keep everything on the calendar on my phone, so I can keep track of it all.

It's been tough getting past the things I can't do anymore. Before the accident, all I used to do was: bike, bike, bike! But now I can't do that. I know I'll never be able to ride again, and that's hard to accept. But I've got past the resentment by channelling my passion in other ways. I can still drive, so I've gone back to cars in a big way. And I go rock climbing every week. I see a friend every week for pizza. I go and see live comedy when I can. There's the photography at Cadwell Park, and, of course, I have to try and keep my car clean!

I've just got back into running. I hadn't felt ready for a long time, but then, a few weeks ago, I just felt ready. I tried the NHS Couch to 5K, and I've done the first nine weeks. I run for at least 30-minute non-stop, thrice a week. When I started, I was running for a minute, then walking for five minutes, but gradually I've increased that to half an hour of continuous running. I can't run as fast as I used to, but I'm slowly increasing my speed and the amount of time I run.

Katherine promised that she would come and run the parkrun with me... And that's a good incentive to keep going!

I'm massively into gardening now too! I never used to be, but now I love it. I'm always out in the garden weeding, and I've got big plans for the front garden. I've started reading too – I've not really been able to read a lot properly since the accident because I just haven't been able to concentrate. I'd read a couple of lines, and then I'd be too tired to read anymore. But I managed to finish a book a few weeks ago.

My main frustration now is that there is still so much I want to do that I can't because of my limitations – because I feel so knackered so much of the time. But whenever an opportunity comes along to try something, I'll always give it a go. After all, what's the worst that can happen...

I can't do it. So what?

I have a great relationship with my daughter now. Things have moved along since that time in hospital, and I didn't even know who she was. I catch up with my dad from time to time too. I've thought about doing voluntary work – but at the moment, I just don't seem to have the time! You'll never find me twiddling my thumbs.

I think this all shows that I've come to terms with what my life is now. I don't think back to my old life as much as I used to. I like to think of my accident as a kind of crazy wake-up call...

Before the accident, I always felt like I was in my twenties. But now I feel like I've aged about twenty years overnight! That's not a bad thing though. I feel more my age. More mature.

My long-term memory is better than it used to be. Sometimes my daughter will show me a photo and when I see it, it all comes flooding back to me. It only takes a little trigger. My short-term memory still isn't great, so I have to rely on my charts and calendars. But when I talk to other people, they tell me that's kind of normal for people my age! It wasn't like that for me before, but I am nearly fifty now! I'm allowed to get a bit forgetful!

I know I'll never ever get to the point in my physical recovery where it's enough. It's like gardening – there's always something more to do. But I've noticed – and other people have too, that I'm still making little improvements all the time. With my running, I've noticed how my endurance has improved, my stamina has improved; even my core strength has improved. My knee is much stronger – I can feel the strength in my joints. And that's all helped with my climbing. Even though I still feel out of balance a lot of the time, I actually feel more stable. My balance isn't right; it never will be. I'm just more able to manage it now. That's the difference.

*

You'll have some tough times as you're getting better. At first, I didn't know my arse from my elbow! It really is like being born again – into an adult body – and it feels like you have to learn everything all over again.

It still frustrates me that I can't string sentences together as well as I could. I get jumbled as I'm talking, and it feels like I'm talking with a mouthful of marbles. People tell me I speak fine, but in my head I don't. It sounds like a jumbled mess.

Frustration is still a big problem for me. But I think the single best piece of advice I got – and I can share it with you know is this:

> Try not to compare yourself with how you were before. Instead, try and compare yourself with how you were when you came out of the hospital. When you look at it that way, you'll be able to see the massive improvements.

As time's gone on, I've been able to think less about what life was like for me before. It's still nice to get the memories back – because life is all about making memories – but you should try to accept the new you. For me, there was a big period of asking, "Why can't I be like I was before?" I felt the anger and the frustration of it. But I've come to terms with who I am now. And in some ways, life has actually changed for the better.

I've learnt what an important role your family and friends can play in your recovery too. And if I can pass on one piece of advice for you to give them, it's this:

> Just listen. More important than anything else, your family just needs to listen to you. And they have to learn to accept the new you too. They need to try to come to terms with your new limitations. You are not the same person anymore, and in some ways, that might be tougher for them to have to deal with than it is for you.

That doesn't mean your family and friends have to give in to you all the time and let you wallow. Amy certainly tells me when I need to get off my arse and clean the house!

I know for a fact that there is always someone worse off than you. And I never forget that. I'm still here, and all things considered, I'm not doing too badly.

I always tell my daughter: "Life is short, enjoy it." And knowing how close I came to death, she knows I really mean it. She knows life can be gone in a heartbeat.

Even if everything you knew is gone, I can promise you, there is another life out there for you. You *will* come to terms with what you have lost. As you work through the process of mending yourself, it will become easier. But it does take time. Don't let anybody tell you otherwise. Your recovery will be stressful at times. You will get frustrated. But it will go on getting easier.

Trust yourself. You will usually know when you are ready for the next challenge. When I first thought about running again, I knew I wasn't ready. But, over time, the thought kept coming back to me, until I knew I was ready to try it.

I've lost things – it's true. It hurt knowing I couldn't ride my bike again. But I got over that. And my advice to you is – focus on those other parts of your life you can still enjoy. Focus on the things you *can* do. I was into cars before I was into bikes, and now that I can't be into bikes any more, I'm back into cars.

I've found that I can still enjoy some of the things I used to do – especially the running and photography – all of these things have helped me get that sense of enjoyment and satisfaction. But let yourself find new things too. For me, it was rock climbing and gardening. All of these things have pushed me in different ways, emotionally, cognitively and physically. (I've obviously picked up the jargon from all that rehab!)

So, whatever stage you're at in your recovery – even if you're right at the beginning of the process – don't despair. No matter how long it takes, hang in there. Even when it doesn't feel like it, even when you feel like you can't take any more, trust me, things will improve.

You may never get 100% better, you may never be happy with what has happened, but, slowly, you will become more accepting of it, and accepting of the person you are now.

Chapter 2

Getting life back on track

The work of the case manager

Anne-Marie Burnett

Often when the case manager meets a client for the first time, the client has no services in place. But in Karl's case, although he had returned to his RAF base, 160 miles away, the team at Headley Court were still managing his rehab. So initially, I worked collaboratively with this team, mainly with their occupational therapist (OT). The situation was complex because while the Defence Medical Rehab Centre (DMRC) was already implementing a graded return to work, my own assessment had highlighted significant cognitive, emotional and physical needs that I considered barriers to a successful return to work of any kind at that time. However, the RAF was obviously keen for Karl to return to his pre accident post and was relying on the recommendations of the DMRC to facilitate this. Despite my assessment clearly identifying the need for Karl to access specialist community private services in the absence of any appropriate statutory provision, it was not appropriate to wade in with my own interventions. It was essential to develop helpful working relationships with key RAF personnel going forwards, knowing that at some point a return to work would be something Karl would want to consider.

I therefore bided my time, working closely with Karl in the meantime to keep the situation under review.

As part of my initial assessment, I completed the DASS (Depression, Anxiety and Stress Scale), a questionnaire that provides an indication as to whether someone is experiencing any of these emotional issues, and of their severity. Karl's responses on the questionnaire did not indicate he had any difficulties; however, during the assessment when we reflected on the enormity of the accident, his injuries, and his recovery to date, Karl was close to tears. He admitted the assessment process had made him realise how life had fundamentally changed and that nearly one year on, this was the first time he had really thought about it. The future he was seeing did not line up with the self-image he still held onto. On one occasion, whilst waiting to go into a meeting with his line manager and the OT from Headley Court, Karl stated that he had thought of throwing himself in front of a train, on more than one occasion, but thoughts of his daughter had stopped him.

Shortly into the meeting, when there was a clear sense of pressure being put on Karl to start a graded return to work, Karl became very frustrated and expressed his anger towards the OT and his managers. This in itself was a perfect example of one of the ways in which his brain injury had affected him. His despair at the situation in which he found himself was palpable, and he was unable to hold this back. He was essentially advised to calm down, and there appeared to be no understanding, or consideration, to Karl's individual needs.

The return to work was put on hold, and the Headley Court team realised that they could not provide the intense community rehab package proposed by the case manager. This would have afforded Karl the opportunity to return to work longer term, when he was ready, and would have been mutually beneficial to both Karl and the RAF.

We were now able to get started on helping Karl get his life back on track…

Coordinating rehab

The case manager gets the rehab team in place, formulates the rehab plan, co-ordinates all involved services and keeps the rehab programme under constant review, thereby adapting it to the changing circumstances. Rehab is rarely straightforward, and the rehab programme needs to be sufficiently flexible to account for barriers that may present themselves. Clients may struggle to engage with the process; they may not respond to certain approaches by therapists, or they may be affected by their own response to events.

Central to this role are the client's goals and the team objectives and actions to support goal achievement. Monitoring progress towards goals allows for accountability, reflection on achievements and a means to alter the rehab approach if things are not working. If possible, this is a collaborative process between the client, family and professionals, but sometimes, circumstances may challenge this and indeed, some clients may not respond well to goal setting in the early stages, instead requiring a period of engagement with the team.

Goals are not necessarily what might be considered aspirational by others; for some clients, being able to wash their hair unaided is of greatest importance, whilst others may be striving to have a holiday abroad. It may be necessary to moderate expectations around what is achievable. Karl had been so active and had lots of interests before his injury, some of which would not have been realistic to set as achievable goals, at least for some years. He was not able to get back on his bike, go running, or go clubbing all night. In this case, the team finds ways of adapting a goal, so it remains meaningful. Expectations need to be managed to avoid clients feeling unfulfilled by a perceived failure and instead enable them to appreciate the new direction that has led them to a slightly different destination.

For many of our clients, the ultimate goal is to help them get back to work. Depending on the severity of their injuries, this will not necessarily be the job they did before. In Karl's case, he wanted to try and return to his previous work role in some capacity. Having forged effective relationships with key RAF personnel from the start of my involvement, I worked closely with Louise (OT) to support ongoing discussions about Karl's work situation. I continued to keep his managers and medical officer updated on Karl's progress, to educate them about Karl's hidden disability when the opportunity presented itself, and to advocate for his ongoing brain injury related needs when we attended routine review meetings with occupational health. I accompanied Karl to his first RAF Medical Board review, to provide information about Karl's ongoing deficits, his rehab programme and the nature of his progress over the months leading up to the review.

For Karl, who had started to find a renewed contentment and had achieved so much in terms of his ability to cope more readily with day to day life, having a decision from the Medical Board as to whether he would be medically discharged or would attempt a further return to work, felt like the final piece of the puzzle.

Following this review, Louise carried on working with Karl to support him back into work with the RAF, albeit not in the role he had been doing before. But ultimately, this proved not to be viable, and Karl was eventually discharged from the RAF.

Progress

The RAF's loss will be someone else's gain. Whatever Karl decides to do in life, he has a huge amount to offer.

Karl's recovery was astonishing. I remember reading his brain scan results and medical records and, even in the early days, wondering how he could function at such a level, and progress as quickly as he did, given the severity of his brain damage. I believe this was in a large part due to his character and personality traits, which boded well for his recovery. He is an intelligent, hardworking, determined individual, and he was fully committed to the rehab process and to getting himself back to the best possible position he could be in.

But it was not all plain sailing. Certain aspects of his premorbid personality actually worked against him in the initial stages of rehab. Karl is a perfectionist. In Karl's world, everything always had to be done to exacting standards; but unfortunately, striving for perfection and having a brain injury are not mutually compatible!

After an injury of that magnitude, the brain works differently. Use of strategies to compensate for cognitive deficits and behavioural challenges is essential. Karl being Karl was not keen on doing that! He had expectations of himself that he should be doing things in the way he did before his injury and that he should not need to adapt to new ways of coping. For example, we just wanted him to plan his days. This is a good technique to try and avoid overloading the brain, and because staying motivated is one of the biggest problems people face after a brain injury, having things scheduled into the day/week can help with initiating and following through with activity.

Karl resisted certain strategies in a very obvious way – and that was actually a good thing. Some clients resist strategies in a less overt way, and that can make it more difficult to find new ways to approach any difficulties they might be having.

I remember a defining moment about nine months into rehab when something 'clicked' for Karl. Although he had still made gains during that time because he was engaging well with the team's input, Karl started to accept that his own drive for perfectionism was holding him back. He had needed time to appreciate this, and with the support and patience of the team, he started to increasingly implement coping strategies with greater independence and to accept every challenge and recommendation presented to him, without resistance.

The challenge of rehab

When I start working with a new client and their family, I warn them that rehab is a stressful process. Generally, people do not realise how challenging it is. The situation is compounded by the lack of post-acute specialist brain injury rehab statutory service provision. In many cases, it can be months or years after the brain injury was sustained that a case manager gets involved. And in that time, the injured person and their family have just been coping as best they can, without any adequate support.

A team then comes in, and each member undertakes a lengthy assessment, which is tiring and potentially repetitive. Therapy sessions begin, and it can feel like your life is not your own. There are constant questions, and seemingly every aspect of your existence is analysed; 'what did you eat this morning, what time did you go to bed last night...?' And whilst all the questions, plans and treatment are geared towards helping you, and no matter how slowly and sensitivity the team approaches your rehab, the process can feel intense and intrusive.

We cannot provide a miracle cure; progress can be slow, full of ups and downs, and is hard work. I advise clients to consider their rehab as a full-time job. Even when professionals or support workers are not coming into the home, rehab will be happening, however subtly, day-in and day-out.

It can seem wonderful to start with; that you finally have specialists working with you who understand what you've been experiencing for months or years, and who are going to help you to make positive changes. However, once the initial honeymoon period is over, cracks can start to show. The stress can ramp up, and it can be hard for clients and their families. The case manager will regularly review the situation and adapt the rehab programme with the team, in consideration to client and family struggles but with the overall aim of maintaining the momentum of rehab, which is crucial to the client's recovery.

The rewards

It is not always possible to make the kind of difference that we want to achieve for every client. Rehab progress is multi-factorial and often strongly influenced by environmental and systemic factors as much as clinical presentation.

Everything came together in Karl's case, in a way that enabled us, to enable him, optimally. At the close of case management, he described that the team had "been able to get me from a position of despair, to one where I now have confidence again, and can look forward to my future life."

I believe in every case, we can make a positive difference, no matter how small, even if we are just there to support the client and family.

Chapter 3

Working with Karl

Katherine Dawson

When I was referred to Karl, he had left a military rehab unit, and there was a lot of red tape to work through, just to get the information I needed. Although I had some general information, I didn't know anything about the testing they'd done while he was on the unit, or how he presented. And I didn't know what rehab had been like for him up to that point. I spoke to the neuropsychologist from Headley Court and spent some time gathering information about what rehab Karl had received on the unit and their thoughts on what work he needed to do now he was heading back into the community.

Karl and I met at the RAF base in April 2016, eleven months after the accident. I was immediately struck by just how broken he seemed and concerned by his level of fatigue. The business of meeting me, getting the passes we needed and then driving me back to his digs exhausted him. Afterwards, he had to go and lie on his bed, and that really gave me a very clear sense of just how hard his life had been since the crash.

I think it's fair to say that the first meeting between us was a little bit 'difficult.'

Sometimes you expect a little bit of resistance… it's rare that people come ready to engage in therapy. But it's also rare that you meet someone who seems quite so defiant as Karl! Now that we know each other a lot better, I can see where that was all coming from. Karl was steeped in a stiff-upper-lipped culture, and he didn't think that any amount of work with me was going to help him, one little bit. He certainly wasn't prepared to admit to any signs of cognitive weakness, or countenance the idea that any of my 'strategies' could possibly help him. I left our first meeting knowing I had a bit of a challenge on my hands!

Meeting someone who's had a brain injury often brings a lot of hidden difficulties. It is possible that the patient may have some issues with personal insight and awareness as to how badly they've been affected. In Karl's case, he was understandably so overwhelmed by his physical change, and aware of what had changed for him, that he was most focussed on his fatigue and dizziness in particular.

After most injuries – and certainly after the kind of injury that Karl had, the physical rehabilitation is the biggest focus initially, and it's where recovery is more noticeable. At that stage, Karl was still walking with a stick, seemed very unsure in his movements and complained a lot about his dizziness. It can be hard (due to the damage to the brain) for individuals to notice changes in thinking, memory and emotions. That's why family and friends can play such an important role; it's much easier for them to supply detailed information about what's changed for the patient, particularly early on in the recovery process.

I think Karl noticed the forgetfulness, but other difficulties, like irritability, an uncharacteristic lack of empathy, and a very up-and-down mood were things that Amy could more easily identify. Damage to the front part of the brain can mean that the person affected is literally unable to notice their difficulties. Also, memory plays a big part. People may forget the details of what has just happened, and this is a big additional barrier.

Externalising internal feelings

Very often in my work, I encounter people who say, "if only (the client) would accept what had happened to them, they would be more on board with how rehab will help." This implies fault and some criticism of the fact that a client is in denial. But, certainly in the early stages, this lack of insight can be better explained by the organic damage to the brain.

A lot of the early work that I do then is in supporting someone in being a bit more aware of their difficulties, while at the same time identifying their strengths and reassuring them that those difficulties are not their fault. It's very common for people who have a brain injury to internalise these feelings: *I feel so dramatically different to how I felt before… my memory is worse, I can't remember things, I struggle to manage my emotions…* It's not surprising that cycling such negative thoughts endlessly around their heads leads people to feel guilty and then cause them to blame themselves, particularly when they start to see the impact their condition has on their relationships.

I think the earlier you can work with someone to reassure them that it's not their fault, the better. The brain is a tricky thing at the best of times. But add an injury to the mix, with all of the disability that follows, and it gets a whole lot trickier for people to manage their responses to the situation they're in.

Having these kinds of discussions with Karl wasn't easy at first. To begin with, the focus was on the very obvious physical symptoms. As I mentioned, he was particularly focussed on the dizziness. As well as the debilitating impact it had on him, he didn't understand why it had come on so long after the crash, and it was his primary source of frustration. The brain scans showed a very real cause for the dizziness, but there was more to it than that…

We did some work around disentangling the physical symptoms of dizziness from the fatigue associated with thinking, the effort it required and the emotional exhaustion he was experiencing. He had so many big issues to deal with around the parts of his life and identity he'd lost, coupled with not knowing who he was and where his life was going. And I needed Karl to appreciate that some of the issues he was experiencing were emotional, even though he was treating them like physical issues.

At that stage, Karl did not want to re-engage with life until he felt better. In other words, "when I feel sufficiently better, I'll get my life back on track. But until then, I am just going to exist in my house." Karl wasn't really ready to talk about any changes in thinking and memory; it put him on the defensive, and it took me a few months before I was able to really talk to Karl about what had changed for him in his brain. It took a little longer still until he was ready to listen. But I expect that kind of response when I'm working with someone who has difficulty with memory, as well as managing their emotions and noticing their difficulties. It is entirely understandable.

Working at the right pace

There is a fine balance between pushing ahead with the work we need to do and working at a rate that feels right to the client. In Karl's case, we needed to hold back a little bit until he was ready to confront what had changed for him. And throughout this time, we had to slowly, slowly, increase the demands we placed on him in a very graded way. We wanted to increase his function and raise his awareness of the way in which more activity – not less – actually helped him manage some of the issues around dizziness and fatigue. And all the while, encouraging him to get used to giving voice to his frustrations.

In some cases, people may have a strong sense of what has changed and be ready to move on, but that still doesn't mean we can forge ahead too quickly. Even when there is no blame attached, many people do experience a profound sense of shame about the accident and its repercussions. They may be aware of the impact their injury is having on others or appreciate how their own unhappiness about their new status quo is affecting the people who are closest to them.

Many patients who have had a significant head injury will feel like they are living in a very confusing new world. One of the biggest difficulties for Karl to come to terms with was his autobiographical memory. When I talked to him about his life, there were big gaps; he could not tell me about his life in general before the injury, and he struggled to put memories into a timeline. He couldn't remember any of it.

If you're reading this and you've been in this situation, you'll know just how disorienting this is. If you're living with someone who's going through this, or you're caring for someone who is, just imagine how that must feel. Imagine how vulnerable it must make you feel. How fragile. So, introducing overwhelming concepts, e.g. *your brain is permanently damaged* – needs to be handled incredibly carefully.

Where there is a lot of memory loss immediately prior to the event or accident that caused the damage, it can suggest that the loss will be permanent. We refer to this as a type of amnesia. Karl never regained those memories of events immediately prior to, and following the accident, and based on the severity of his injury, I would not have expected him to regain them. But in terms of the longer-term memories, patches of memory returned as his recovery progressed. Karl described hearing a piece of music that triggered a memory, and he would associate it with what he had been doing, and suddenly another gap would be filled in. Every time it happened, Karl said it comforted him, and helped him feel a little more connected to himself. Music seemed to really unlock things for him, so we didn't have to do any additional work on helping him try to remember; it happened quite organically, over time.

The majority of my clients have no memory of their traumatic event, but the incident can still shatter the beliefs they have about the world they live in, and it requires some work to deal with that. To support individuals in dealing with the gaps around the trauma, it can be really helpful – when they are ready – to build up a timeline of the events surrounding the event, using photos, newspaper articles, police reports and information from family.

Strengths and weaknesses

Under normal circumstances in neuro rehab, you start with the foundations: you need to ensure that the patient has a good grounding in what has happened, before you start work on making adjustments. So we talked about the possibility of doing some education around Karl's brain injury and the implications of it, but Karl was very resistant to the idea to start with. Mainly, he dismissed it because he said they'd already focussed on how his brain had been damaged in military rehab. But I could see that he was still struggling with the limitations and restrictions his brain injury had forced upon him. Karl wasn't functioning as he felt he should be, and he found that deeply frustrating.

Before rehab can really begin, it's important that work is done to establish the patient's memory, attention and planning skills, to see where their strengths and weaknesses are. Ideally, rehab should be as low-stress as possible, and pitched to people's strengths, more than their weaknesses, so that they don't get tired and make mistakes. I wanted to give him some real data to work with, so I suggested we'd do some work to summarise his strengths and weaknesses. I completed some paper and pencil tests that tap into different areas of the brain.

I wanted Karl to be able to gauge how much his brain had changed since the accident, and I wanted to plan some more work keyed into his strengths, so, for comparison, I also summarised the testing completed at the military rehab unit. Karl agreed to that, and at the same time, he agreed to doing some anger management work. I don't think that he saw his anger as a problem at that time, but Amy and some of the other people around him certainly did.

That session where I fed back Karl's strengths and weaknesses to him seemed to be going really well – at first – but then, he just dismissed everything. It wasn't that he didn't accept the findings, it was just that he was only able to focus on the weaknesses, and I think that made him feel as if he'd lost face. Karl is a very bright man, and I do think that for that profile of person – someone who places real value on their intellectual abilities and then experiences significant cognitive change – there is more of an adjustment to be made.

Although we were talking about the positive things as well, he only really heard me feeding back weaknesses, rather than things he was still good at. That made him really angry. He asked me, "What is the point in me knowing this? What's happened has happened. I don't see any benefits in any of this." And then he just handed the feedback straight back to me. He didn't want it. Sometimes, people just roll it up or fold it up as small as they can because it's just too soon for them to come to terms with it all. And in those cases – and in Karl's case – it is sometimes better to park that side of things and take a different approach...

We pulled back from talk of strengths and weaknesses altogether and tried to identify what he was going to be feel most motivated to work on. We needed to help Karl begin to feel a little bit more like his old self, even in spite of all the barriers that we had to work with. I knew what a massive blow it was for him to lose the skill to get back on his motorbike, so we started talking about some of the things that he'd enjoyed doing before the crash that he was (or could still be) capable of doing.

Karl had enjoyed baking before and told me his Spanish mum had been an amazing cook. So he was enthusiastic about the idea of trying to cook some Spanish dishes of his own. It was an important step: it wasn't just about the skill of cooking; it was a way for him to reassert some identity. It helped him feel a bit more connected with who he was, or who he used to be. And it felt meaningful to him.

Remember that at this point, Karl really had no idea who he was. And that is an impossibly difficult concept for anyone to have to deal with. Every problem he had, every frustration and every flare up he suffered was compounded by the fact that there were so many chunks of his life missing. So many pieces of the jigsaw that made up Karl were simply not there.

We did plenty of work around the frustrations he was having, helping Karl to work out what was triggering the frustrations. We talked through some examples, particularly around some of the instances when his anger had got the better of him. It was important to help Karl to identify some of his trigger points – at least intellectually – so that he could recognise them more easily when they crept up on him again. This kind of self-monitoring work is a key skill to develop for anyone that is going to take ownership of their recovery. And Karl engaged really well with things that he could take the lead on personally. He had always been such a switched on, self-starter that the loss of independence he'd suffered was particularly hard to deal with. So, engaging him in ways which gave him back little elements of control keyed right into his desire for greater independence and autonomy.

I had a session with Amy, who told me about a couple of instances of Karl losing his cool – one in a shop, when they were at the checkout. She said that the cashier had done something wrong and asked them to put all their shopping back into the trolley so she could scan it again. Karl had lost it, she said and became incredibly verbally aggressive. Amy had had to try and calm things down. She remembered thinking it wasn't how he would have behaved before. He may still have had a short-temper before, but he wouldn't have behaved in that way.

Then there was an awful journey where he had got lost on an estate after they'd gone to look at a new house. He'd ended up screaming at her, and she told me that she'd just had to get out of the car. The situation wasn't resolvable for either of them: she wanted an apology, and he didn't want to give her an apology.

When I talked to Karl about it, we whittled that situation down to the root cause: getting lost had made him feel extremely vulnerable. He would never have got lost before the crash, he'd had exceptional spatial abilities. So to him, it felt like a weakness, just another example of something else he couldn't do anymore. In retrospect, that seemed more obvious to him, but in the heat of the moment, it certainly hadn't been. Painful as it was, helping him to unpick all of these things helped him to learn to notice these triggers for himself – and that was an important step.

But noticing his triggers was just the *first* step. We needed to extend Karl's awareness of the impact his behaviour could have on others. By his own admission, Karl found it difficult to put himself in other people's shoes. So, we did some work focussing on helping him see how the people around him could support him. It was important to show him that a) there was no shame in looking to his friends and family for that kind of support and b) it wasn't fair on himself to expect to be able to do things his brain just wasn't (at that time) capable of doing. We did more work on helping Karl deal with the anger itself a little later, as you'll see as you read on.

Working through depression

Of course, it's hard on friends and family to accept and live with these kinds of changes. And I know it was really tough on Amy in particular. Amy had been dealing with a significant illness of her own, while she was supporting Karl. And even in spite of the fact she and Karl had separated, she still managed to support him an incredible amount. Let's not forget that they had to work through a lot of issues, and there was plenty of hard work to be done. It's not far-fetched to say that, in many ways, the old Karl really had died. So much of who he was before had gone. Somehow, they both had to learn to deal with that…

The anger and depression doesn't just go away. Often it lies dormant for a bit and then resurfaces. I'd been working with Karl on his anger issues for about three months and focussing on those activities that would help him tap back into a sense of who he was. But then he had a massive drop in mood, and a really significant increase in fatigue, accompanied by an increase in suicidal thoughts. He hadn't really presented with suicidal thoughts since he'd been in military rehab, so it represented quite a shift in his presentation.

It isn't unexpected for people going through this kind of process to feel depressed and suicidal. And in one sense, it does actually show that people are moving to the next stage in their recovery. Counterintuitive as it may sound, it can be seen as a positive sign that they are developing more awareness of their difficulties and the enormity of their situation. In other words, this is a critically important stage in anyone's recovery, and reaching it can be very painful. But, if we handle it right, it can signal an upturn in the recovery process.

Understandably, people hear 'suicidal thoughts' and panic. Friends, family and service providers may respond in quite a reactive way – wanting to try and 'fix' the issue. Instead, a suicide intervention plan will look at why people are experiencing such thoughts and experiencing such intense distress, and then work to put those feelings in the context of their life as it is now.

It is really important to listen to people try and articulate their depressed, bleak and suicidal feelings, no matter how difficult it is to hear. Stopping someone from talking about suicidal thoughts will only make them feel more guilty for having those thoughts at all.

For most people I've worked with, the actual experience of the suicidal thought itself is only one part of the issue; we also have to deal with how they (and others) feel about having experienced those thoughts in the first place. Very often, the enormity of it can silence people. It really is vitally important that we keep talking through these stages and normalising their feelings. This may be allied with pharmacological intervention if necessary.

In some cases, the suicidal thoughts can be incredibly intrusive, and we are always mindful of any signs of intentionality that accompanies these thoughts, e.g. people who begin to make plans to end their life. In Karl's case, there weren't any signs of intentionality. But there was a very significant level of hopelessness, and he was struggling to identify reasons for living. And that was accompanied by shame about feeling those thoughts at all.

We talked about the possibility of Karl taking an antidepressant, and having a psychiatric review, but he flat-out refused. Instead we drew up a safety plan and agreed that if Karl's levels of hopelessness increased and his suicidal thoughts became more intrusive and difficult to control, the plan would kick in.

The plan set out ways of restricting the means of suicide (if he got to the point of generating clear plans) and provided soothing and distracting activities, support contacts and a list of services to contact. In the event that we reached crisis stage, we agreed that we would move to a psychiatric assessment.

Fortunately, we did not get to the crisis stage, but Karl did agree with the contract that we drew up, and that, in itself, was reassuring. This can be a very containing and proactive piece of work to do because it puts the spotlight on the suicidal thoughts, without panicking anybody, and without ignoring the seriousness of the thought.

We did some additional work on de-stigmatising the fact that Karl was having these thoughts, as well as continuing to try and normalise his feelings – while still taking them very seriously. When we put them into the context of everything he'd been through: the enormous trauma he'd suffered, all the losses, and all the current stresses in his life, it was absolutely understandable. For Karl, this really was the first inkling of his emerging realisation that life was going to be very different; he hadn't just suffered a temporary setback. And he needed to know that anyone facing up to that life-altering reality would react in the same way.

Existential issues

Karl's old coping mechanisms were gone, and he hadn't yet developed a new set of coping mechanisms. At this point, Karl had more-or-less cocooned himself in his home. He was inactive and staying in bed a lot. He felt as if the rest of the world was moving on without him. Things were difficult between him and Amy too – and I think those difficulties were pivotal in convincing him that he had no quality of life.

Added to all of that, he was ruminating endlessly – as you would expect – on *the* most fundamental question in life: *who am I*? This is really common after a brain injury. People feel like they have lost themselves. They literally have no reference point, and that must be terrifying.

Indeed, people who have had encephalitis – which is a bit like a flu that results in an acquired brain injury – often present with really significant memory problems afterwards, and they express the sense that, as far as they're aware, nothing in particular happened, but now, somehow, they've got a brain injury.

While everyone's experiences of brain injury; however, it has occurred, will be subtly or dramatically different, many of the same existential issues are common:

- This person isn't the real me.
- I can't do the things that matter to me anymore.
- My life is ruined.

All of these thoughts hit Karl at the same time and just ramped up his sense of hopelessness. So we focussed more on self-compassion, and making sure that he felt safe and secure to work through his feelings without judgement, and with the compassion of the team he had around him.

Gradually, as he started to feel a little bit more secure, we were able to open up some really important discussions around old Karl and new Karl. This is when we really started to talk in more detail about the concept that the old Karl had died, and, at that stage, we still didn't know who the new Karl was, or what part of the old Karl could be ported across. As you might expect, the more we unpicked this idea, the more vulnerable Karl felt. These kinds of fundamental questions are the basis of an existential crisis, and Karl just didn't know how to define himself anymore. And he didn't know what living a completely different life was going to mean to him. So, bearing in mind some of his barriers, I needed to support him in accessing that vulnerability, and just allowing him to grieve for the parts of him that had changed, and for everything he'd had to give up.

Practically, he'd had to give up his motorbike. And it wasn't just a motorbike for him. We talked a lot about what that bike represented – it was about spontaneity, and a connection with a community, and a whole culture. In looking for elements of the old Karl to carry over to his new life, the bike and the birds were obvious starting points…

Karl had always been a keen birdwatcher and photographer. We encouraged him to start taking photos of the birds outside his window. And over a period of time, you could see him getting more engaged with it. On one occasion, he smeared peanut butter over a log in his garden and took a photo of the bird when it came to feed – and then he sent us the photos. So that was the start – really small steps – leading to bigger things.

Then Karl went to Cadwell Park, where he'd been many times before to watch the racing, and he started taking pictures there too. The first time he went back was harder for him. Before the crash, he'd have been in his element, but on that day, he told me all he could think about was the woman who had done this to him; the woman who had literally shattered his life. He was looking in on a world that used to be his, but it his wasn't his anymore.

It was another pivotal moment. For most of his life, Karl had been strong, immovable. He had lived life by his rules, and, in extremis, he had always lived by the mantra to man up. That had fitted right in with his career in the RAF, where vulnerability had been seen as a bit of a weakness. So, for him to feel so overwhelmed by loss felt alien to him.

By then, we had developed a secure and trusting relationship, and he felt he could talk to me about it. And actually, just having someone to listen, and to acknowledge how difficult it was for him, rather than trying to fix it, was a big part of the process. Karl said that a lot of the time, people would tell him, "Oh you're not that bad..." but those sorts of supposedly well-meaning approaches really aren't very helpful at all. Sometimes, he just needed to be allowed to say how horrendous he felt, and for someone to bear witness to his loss.

Karl's worldview had been so concrete that it had been difficult for him to see the shades of grey, and see what elements of himself he could still pull across to his new life. We spent some time exploring where he had acquired the sense that showing emotion was a sign of weakness. He talked about being sent away to boarding school and feeling like he became a bit robotic there, as if he lost a sense of emotion. And naturally his work on the crash and smash team had been quite traumatic at times; he had literally had to pull dead bodies out of aircraft.

It was easy to see how his work on the crash and smash team had affected his behaviour. He was doing a challenging and stressful job, and there's no way that wouldn't have influenced the person he was at that time. Part of his coping mechanism would have been going out and living life to the full, which is exactly how he had been living before the accident.

We worked on piecing it all back together – that jigsaw of Karl's life. And every little bit helped us to uncover more of the old Karl.

Actually, in unpicking all of these different elements of his life, Karl made some surprising discoveries. He even came to feel that he had acquired a softer side after everything that had happened, in contrast to the tough, no-nonsense guy he had been before. He felt as if he had acquired more sensitivity and that he was more able to think about things from other people's point of view.

That was a crucial shift. That was the point at which he suggested that, not all of the changes that had happened had been bad ones. And he really started to buy into the concept of trusting that things were going to go on improving.

What happens when your invincibility is taken away from you?

Despite all the amazing progress he was making, Karl still seemed to be somewhat stuck in his feelings towards the woman who had caused the crash. And in a case like this – where somebody external has literally rewritten your life story – that isn't surprising. Nevertheless, it's still harmful. And it will still affect your ability to work towards recovery.

We talked about ways in which life changes after trauma and affects the rules you're used to living your life by. Karl had always thought of himself as being invincible; that was his personal narrative. But trauma takes that certainty and shatters it. And that's why he was left feeling all that anger, all that rage.

Karl didn't want to do any work around how he felt towards the woman. He was fixed on the notion that there was nothing I could say to him that would change how he felt. Again, it was very black and white thinking. I remember that session very well, because I pushed Karl quite hard, and then he told me, that for him, it wasn't about her anymore. It was about the fact that now, he couldn't stand on a balance board properly, and he couldn't butter toast, and it was about all the difficulties he was having just concentrating on listening to me. He hadn't spoken about those kinds of cognitive experiences before, but he had got to the stage where he was noticing more as he was recovering. That was six months into our work, and it opened up an important conversation about what his life was really like on a day-to-day basis.

Everyone is different. There are no rights and wrongs. Some people are ready to start doing work around their brain injury early on. For Karl it took a little longer, but when he was ready, he was a lot more receptive to it. Some people may read this and be surprised that we never addressed his feelings of anger towards the lady who caused the accident. This was a highly emotive issue for Karl, and he found it very difficult to reason through the argument that it was relevant work. I kept coming up against this block, which I felt was a combination of how he coped emotionally, combined with the difficulties he had been experiencing with reasoning things out since his injury.

When he was ready, we took a proper look at the scans from the day of the injury and looked at what areas were damaged. That felt meaningful to him. He could see the full extent of his injury in real terms – and that helped him make sense of it. For example, his verbal memory wasn't great, so we looked at the area of the brain responsible for verbal memory so that he could see the damage for himself.

A lot of this work was about giving Karl a stronger sense of compassion for his own situation. It was no wonder he was struggling, given the extent of his injuries. But there was no use telling him that, he needed to appreciate it for himself. And because Karl found that helpful, it unlocked another door for us and made him see that perhaps he did need some strategies after all…

Bear in mind I had been categorically banned from even using the word 'strategies' for months! To Karl, it had just sounded 'a bit too hippy.' I kept bringing it back though. Eventually, we settled on calling each new strategy a plan of attack instead!

What's going on in the brain?

The brain is obviously a very sensitive organ. It's estimated that good, spontaneous brain recovery takes about twelve to eighteen months. If you were to plot it on a graph, you'd see quite a steep recovery curve for that initial period, but after that, it starts to plateau. Saying that, I remember sitting in a team meeting years ago with a rehab medicine consultant who put forward a very persuasive argument for offering community-based neuro rehab to a client who was ten years post-injury. Whilst I have seen some remarkable recoveries when rehab intervenes early on with the clients I have worked with, I don't think there is a ceiling when considering rehab to improve independence and quality of life.

The most common mistake people make is over-pacing themselves. They try to do too much too soon, and it just exhausts them. Any fatigue on a brain as damaged as Karl's just further exacerbates problems with memory and attention. You get tired and irritable, which means you make more errors, which means you forget more, which means you berate yourself more, which means you feel more ashamed… It's like a vicious cycle.

Targeted fatigue management work led by Karl's OT (which focussed on providing education about why the brain gets more fatigued after injury, and gives strategies that focus on pacing and balancing daily activities) was crucial. Alongside this work is therapy to support people to recognise the things they have to change – they are not optional. And that takes work. It requires significant adaptations for most people, and that's often when grief work helps. I need to give people space to grieve for the fact that they've had an exceptionally traumatic experience.

We work hard to get them to a place where they can use strategies without berating themselves and establish habits and routines to help them move forwards.

I think that, in Karl's case, he had already made the decision to 'move on' at some level. He already knew that he was not going to be able to get back on a bike. In his mind, that had already been taken away as an option. (Bear in mind here that grieving for things that are still there as a concept but are just closed off to you – like riding away on a bike – is really difficult.)

We looked at the typical stages that someone can move through whilst grieving, and accepting that his loss was like a death. Even though you don't move through the stages of grief neatly and sequentially, Karl found it really helpful to identify the stages that he had been through in a fairly concrete way, and assessing for himself where he was and what he had to do to get to the next stage, as he worked towards acquiring positive new habits.

It really helps to anchor new habits into existing routines, so people do them over and over, and procedurally learn them. That's why rehab units work so well – the work is underpinned by such good structures. Every day, the same things happen, and people implicitly learn. Even if they have sustained a major brain injury, people still learn by doing.

It's a bit more difficult doing that out in the community, particularly if the person is alone and/or resistant to the work. We have to get them to a stage where they are doing all the steps habitually. That's why we put in as many compensatory aids as we could for Karl (such as alarms and memory aids) – just to take the load off him having to think about, and remember, everything. We started by trying to encourage our idea of what his day should look like, and needless to say, that didn't go down too well! So we handed it over to him, with some guidelines, and he made his own timetable, and put it on Google Calendar so we could all check it. He even sent out an email onetime saying, *I'm aware that not all of you are checking in to see what I'm doing!* To this day, I still don't know how he knew that! The therapists all enjoyed that, and it really helped to motivate him.

We also wanted to put Karl in as many different functional environments as possible, where he would have to use his skills in an authentic, meaningful way. On a recommendation from our OT, he started going to a place called Hill Holt – doing forestry activities – and that was a massive boost for his rehab. He felt valued, he was part of the community, and if he got really angry, he was able to remove himself to a safe distance to defuse. He used some of the compassion-focussed therapy (CFT) techniques we were doing, but in a real-life setting. It's all very well running through scenarios at home, but it's hard to know just how much results are affected by fatigue, a low mood or a lack of purpose. Out in the real world is where it counts.

He also started rock climbing, recommended by his physio who had explained that the physical and mental processes involved are incredibly useful for people in recovery. It definitely helped Karl with his strength and balance, and I observed a really positive impact on his self-confidence. It certainly helped strengthen his skills of attention and concentration. When we are working with our clients, we're always looking for ways to tap back into activities that feel useful and give a sense of achievement and purpose.

Here's that word again… 'strategies' really need to feel meaningful. We have to keep in mind someone's strengths and weaknesses and then explore how to adapt activities to tap into who they are. You can't often give patients back what they've lost, and whilst climbing didn't exactly replicate riding his bike, it did test Karl's concentration, it raised his adrenalin levels and it left him feeling energised.

He also returned to creating fractal geometry videos – this was incredibly complicated, detailed work and it just suited Karl's skills perfectly. Karl had always been interested in fractals, which he described to me as a never-ending pattern, grounded in mathematics, and we even spent one of our sessions watching a documentary on the Mandelbrot set (I still have to Google it to help me understand)! I found it fascinating that this never-ending pattern, described as God's thumbprint, can be found in nature, in trees, coastlines and clouds but also within the human brain. A lot has been written about how fractals are a way of explaining infinity using maths, and I think there was a clear parallel with Karl starting this work again, and how it showed that he had begun to see fresh hope and different possibilities. Karl became so immersed in the work, and that focus in itself, is a good example of positive cognitive rehab.

The skills required to complete the fractals were around sustaining attention, switching attention and recall. I know from experience that it is far more powerful to embed cognitive rehab into an activity that is meaningful, rather than an isolated, computer-generated task. I think this played quite a part in the later stages of his rehab. Karl had an obvious and infectious passion for this work, and it really took him out of himself. Aligned with his love for music, he enjoyed playing with the concepts. It all felt very meaningful to him.

By this stage we were increasingly able to play to Karl's strengths, an approach that should always be at the heart of any successful rehab. Karl was on board with the concept that certain things in his brain had changed, and they were classed as weaknesses… but there were also a lot of strengths remaining. And it was time to tap into those strengths.

New roles in rehab

There's a model of therapy called interpersonal therapy, which focuses on helping individuals to identify and work through changes within life that are associated with difficult feelings. Karl had so many old roles, both personal and professional, that he could no longer maintain as part of his new life after the crash. Whilst we did not formally engage in this therapy, I 'borrowed' some of the exercises. Because they were visual, they helped Karl understand the next stage of therapy, around transitioning from old to new roles.

We tried an exercise to help him navigate his roles more easily and picked up on the earlier work, we had begun about old and new roles.

When doing this work, Karl was able to see that he could still bring across his determination, courage and practical ways of solving problems. We talked about the importance of obtaining some mastery over his loss of memory – focussing on a better understanding of strengths and weaknesses, and using strategies like activity scheduling, pacing and fatigue management.

Karl was also able to identify how important it had been for him to be free and spontaneous in his life before the crash. He had even got used to feeling he was a little bit invincible. Motorbikes, DJ'ing, and, most of all, having the freedom to do what he wanted was important to him. But at the same time, his job gave him a strong sense of structure. He had the best of both worlds: his life was bound by a rigid structure, but he also had an outlet for spontaneity and feeling free and independent.

In terms of his relationships before the accident, Karl described himself as someone who got bored very easily, which fitted in with his need for spontaneity and freedom. I don't think his relationships featured particularly heavily in his old life.

Independence had always been a key thing for Karl, and it's one of the reasons why he resisted rehab so strongly at the beginning of the process – it must have felt as if the therapists invading his space after the crash had taken all of his autonomy away from him.

But we had to be pragmatic. Karl's life had changed, and he had to face a stark choice: he was either going to remain stuck, feeling the loss of the life he had previously had, or he could start to let go of some of those things, and try to find other elements that he could pull across to his new life.

We kept coming back to Karl's love of motorbikes. We knew that motorbikes could no longer play the same role in his new life. But we also knew that, as well as the visceral thrill of riding, motorbikes represented the spontaneity Karl craved in his life. So, we looked at other ways he could meet that need.

Karl told me that because rehab seemed so slow and one-paced, he felt like he was living in a shoebox, and he wasn't making any memories. We considered other ways for Karl to take spontaneous choices in life and make some new memories. And as a result, he decided to take a trip to America to see some of his old friends. For him, that was a different kind of spontaneous outlet. It provided a bit of escapism from his life at that time – and when he came back, he came back a little bit different.

I don't think Karl had fully appreciated the extent of his difficulties before he left – and how his fatigue was going to affect him. The OT worked with Karl on fatigue management and practical strategies to reduce the load on his memory and thinking, and we talked about emotional coping strategies which he still wasn't a fan of…

But when he came back, he had a new realisation that things were different – particularly compared with his last trip to America. There was a new maturity about him; he was more accepting of the reality of his new situation. I think that going to America on his terms and having that experience for himself was a pivotal moment. He felt he had to do it. And he was really proud of himself for doing it. It helped him to scratch that itch, and transition over to thinking: *I can still be spontaneous – there are restrictions to it, but I can still give vent to my spontaneity. I just have to do it in a slightly different way.*

And that really helped him pull something across that he had worried was lost forever.

Self-critical thinking and anger management

Karl's appreciation of how so much of what he had been going through had been outside of his control had started to increase. Previously, whenever I had tried to discuss the kinds of difficulties someone might experience after a brain injury, he had always dodged it, defended his position and been quite angry in response. But I kept on going back to it. And then, I knew things had really changed when Karl talked openly, for the first time, about the difficulties he experienced in having a conversation with another person. He found it hard to keep hold of the conversational thread, to remember what they were saying and then reply appropriately. It was a big admission. And it meant we were able to move onto other issues around cognition and memory – and how it all played into Karl's cycle of self-criticism. We identified that if Karl wanted to implement meaningful, lasting change to pull him into this new phase of his life, something about his self-critical voice had to change.

Karl's self-critical voice had become such a big part of him that he didn't even notice it any more. So, we worked on strategies to help him notice when he was being self-critical. This involved keeping a log for a short period of time, and writing down what he noticed straight after an incident when he would be angry, either at himself or someone else. He was soon able to see the sorts of things he was saying to himself "I am an idiot/they're idiots/why can't I do this etc."

The self-criticism tied in with the escalation in his anger. We also worked on strategies to help him calm himself down whenever he was 'in the red,' so he could move out of it more quickly, using a CFT model. Karl really bought into the concept that humans exist in three different systems:

- A drive system (in which we achieve our goals and succeed)
- A threat system, which is heightened when individuals experience trauma and part of their brain remains on alert for more danger
- A soothing system (which helps us feel calm and content and settles us)

We discussed how being human was hard work and acknowledged that while he had not chosen this accident or his brain injury and while the escalations in anger were not actually his fault – it was still his responsibility to deal with the issue. And that meant working with the rehab team to develop ways of managing his difficulties.

We started to identify some of the things that would help him get out of those angry places. Some of them were very concrete things, like identifying good behavioural routines to get him back into the green. If you're looking for examples, we're talking about strategies to practise that focus on the following:

- Managing fatigue and pacing yourself
- Getting enough sleep at night
- Having a good wind-down routine
- Eating well
- Using cognitive rehab strategies to minimise the effects of memory problems (including streamlining systems in your home)
- Following a daily timetable
- Focussing on personal well-being

All of the team worked hard on ensuring Karl began planning in positive and enjoyable experiences and staying physically active. Underpinning it all was the focus on making that transition from the old to the new, and understanding that although the old Karl had no problems with memory, attention, or focus, the new Karl does.

I knew Karl liked data and visual representations of concepts, so we came up with a table showing what he was like and what he needed to do in terms of tasks to adjust his thinking.

Old role	*Adjustment*	*New role*
You have been in control of what you did and only relied on yourself.	You are grieving for the loss of the part of you that was completely self-reliant. This leaves you feeling vulnerable, which you struggle with.	Being more comfortable with the idea of being vulnerable and other people helping you with that.
No problems with memory, attention etc.	Struggling to come to terms with the fact your memory and other cognitive abilities are not working as well, without berating yourself.	Relying on memory aids / strategies. Not verbally attacking yourself.
Doing jobs till they are finished.	Needing to pace yourself.	You are pacing – doing one thing at a time and having enforced breaks.

I used cognitive behavioural therapy to help him challenge his negative thoughts, but Karl didn't respond to it particularly well. When he was in the red, he would say, "I know what you're talking about, but I don't believe you." So we shifted to use more behavioural techniques. In rehab, it's really important not to go head-to-head with someone and try to insist they adopt specific strategies. Often, the rehab team has to come up with creative strategies to bridge into our clients' worlds, using knowledge of their strengths without hammering the weaknesses. We knew Karl's thinking was quite black and white after the accident and providing evidence to demonstrate that his thinking was not very helpful only made him defend his position further.

Identifying useful behavioural techniques

In discussing behavioural techniques, Karl found that listening to music helped him to calm down. But he couldn't just go and listen to music at work, and he couldn't just pop on some music when he was at the height of anger, so we needed other ways to help his brain de-escalate. Sometimes, it could be as simple and straightforward as a time out – just taking a few minutes, on his own, to re-focus. And ultimately, that's what worked for Karl, just telling whoever he was with, "I am in the red… I need to leave…" Then he would go to another room, or step outside, and he would calm down.

Anger is a difficult emotion anyway. What do people do with their anger? A lot of people hold onto it, and that can be very damaging. I've done some work around the idea that, for people in Karl's situation, it's not just anger that gets brought to an argument but also anxiety that comes to the table. It can be sadness. Underneath the anger, there can be a great deal of grief and loss, and knowing this can leave people feeling really conflicted. But actually, when you map out the human brain and understand how tricky it is to regulate all these feelings, it becomes clear that all of that swirling mess of emotions is really normal.

Helping people map out different parts of themselves can bring different things to the same argument. And again, a lot of the work I do is around normalising the experience they're having and the conflicting nature of it. In many cases after injury, you find that the brain's threshold for stress is much lower than it was. That means that it's important not to over-pathologise some of the triggers. The severity of the reactions people have can just literally be because they're exhausted, or that they can't concentrate anymore, or that there is too much noise going on around them. All of these things might not seem like a big deal to an outsider, but the effects are cumulative. And as Amy will tell you, the result is that they will suddenly blow, seemingly over something insignificant.

While it helps for people to get a really good idea of their triggers – the things that are bound to set them off – it's also important to accept the fact that people with brain injuries have so many barriers to overcome. The difficulties they face can be as a result of organic damage to the brain, coupled with the stress they are under, and the loss they have experienced.

We need to look at what people can alter, and we'd start by trying to reduce levels of arousal. That's when you introduce coping strategies around relaxation, controlled breathing and visual imagery – trying to expand their toolkit to help them bring their physiological levels of arousal down.

I have found visually guided breathing apps particularly helpful for people who have had a brain injury. Firstly, they provide a visual distraction, which can maintain an individual's attention in a much better way than a lengthy relaxation script. They can also cut rumination, and something similar, called perseveration, which is very common after a frontal brain injury when an individual gets stuck on a thought (often a negative one that causes stress). Then they find it difficult to switch off that thought. Karl being Karl agreed to give a certain visual breathing app a go, but then quickly did his own research, found an app that suited him better and went with that!

But many other people will benefit from progressive muscular relaxation as a tool to help them relax, or can imagine a safe place for themselves to help them defuse. As well as the breathing app, taking a time out was enough for Karl to bring those levels down. And really, he didn't buy any of those other ideas. He couldn't sustain those levels of abstract thinking and didn't really get the potential benefits.

We always tailor our approach accordingly, and there's always a potential strategy for us to pursue; the key is to cut the cycle and give people permission to focus on something else to help their brain calm down.

Once we've established a routine for managing stress, we can move on to work around trying to challenge people's unhelpful thoughts. But it all depends on what people can tolerate. For some people, it will be enough to establish a behavioural routine (particularly if their brain injury has meant they have great difficulty with reasoning).

Life gets better

Cognitively, when I look at Karl's initial scans, I'm struck by just how far he has come.

The injury was classified as an extremely severe brain injury. His coma scale was as low as it could possibly be before death, but when you look at how he is now… If you were to quantify memory and attention, planning and problem-solving etc., his improvement has been remarkable.

But we have to weight that against Karl's own experience of his recovery. He has said that he doesn't feel as quick or articulate as he used to. So, on paper, his scores are vastly improved, but we have to remember that this was a really high-functioning person.

It was hard for Karl to hear people telling him what a remarkable recovery he'd made. He certainly wasn't basing his own estimation of his progress on quantifiable test scores, he was basing it on the quality of his life, and there can be quite a disparity between the two. Of course, it *is* a remarkable recovery, but there are still ongoing barriers that Karl has to live with – that anyone has to live with after a trauma of that nature. There is a lot of work to be done around coming to terms with that.

So how do you do that?

In the early days of recovery, the focus is always really goal focussed. But as things change, you start to think more about the concept of identity, and of people's stories. The danger for many people in this situation is that they can end up feeling alone and isolated. Sometimes, it doesn't matter how many people you have around you, if they don't understand what you're going through, they can't help.

I gave Karl a survivor's guide to read, and he found it really helpful, just knowing he wasn't alone. He took real comfort in knowing that even though people do go through tragedy, there is still the belief that keeps people going, of knowing that something positive can come out of it. This kind of work can only be done, and believed in, when the person is really ready to make that leap into hope.

Karl really grasped onto hope – even though he didn't know what life was going to look like down the line. And I think he has shown that life can get better. Even after a dreadful physical, emotional and cognitive trauma, life can get back on a different track that can be rewarding in new and unexpected ways.

Moving on...

I usually work with clients immediately after their accident for a period of months or years and then don't see them again. But sometimes, I'm called back to help them if they get stuck in their recovery. One of the biggest coping mechanisms that many people lose is the ability to problem-solve their way out of situations – and that can make it significantly harder for people to cope when they get very low. They can feel as if there is no way out.

This means there is always a vulnerability for people who have had a brain injury in times of transition or crisis. It means that rehab should be seen as ongoing. It isn't a one-off event, more a continuum where people can dip in and out, as and when they need to. It might just be a bit of reassurance, a little bit of additional work or even some activity with friends or family – just something to further the ongoing rehab process.

In Karl's case, the first major upheaval came when he was medically discharged from his job. It was a significant rite of passage moment for him. He had always felt that he was going to return to work, but after so much uncertainty along the way, he decided that being medically discharged was the right decision. It felt to him, that his time in the RAF was finished.

Karl actually tried to return to work on two occasions, and the first time was probably just too early. It wasn't as well managed as it could have been. There were just too many barriers for him to face. And it may be that that knocked his confidence the second time around. Again, these are the little things that people aren't necessarily aware of. On the outside, it may have appeared as if everything was fine, but actually, it would have been an incredibly hard process for Karl to manage, more-or-less on his own.

Independence

Karl was always working to a timeline of how long he wanted to engage with therapy. After a year of working together – in the spring of 2017 – Karl said that he definitely didn't want to have the rehab team in his life by Christmas 2017. We actually stopped working together in September 2017 – it had felt like we were moving towards a natural conclusion.

We repeated some assessments around his memory and attention to help him with his return to work, and I talked about the possibility of doing some brain injury education for his work; Karl said not to worry as he'd do it himself. (And that was great to hear.) By then, our sessions had dropped to a monthly schedule, and it felt like an appropriate place to stop. We'd covered what we'd wanted to cover, and Karl was such a strongly self-directed person that we knew he had the tools in place, and the will to look after his own recovery from then on.

It was an ambivalent moment, as it often is. Karl felt like we had achieved a lot together, but he also felt eager to take that next step on his own. So, therapeutically, it felt like an appropriate time to say goodbye – and Karl packed me up some cakes to take home with me! Karl reminisced about the time he had first baked muffins for the rehab team. I hadn't forgotten that moment either; I arrived, ate the muffin and then accidentally tipped the entire plate of crumbs onto the floor. He cleared it up. And then, as I was leaving, I knocked the same plate of crumbs back onto the floor! Karl will never let me forget this. I pretend I did this to model imperfection!

I have many memories of the hard work and perseverance, which Karl has shown in reaching this point in his life. Along with all the other professionals who have been involved in Karl's rehabilitation, I recognise all he has achieved, and I hear we're very close to doing that parkrun together…!

Directing your own recovery: well-being

Knowing what you need to do – but translating it into action is hard. But the more you can do to establish a routine, the better; it will help reduce cognitive demands during your recovery – and keep you focussed. So, here are a few pointers to help you do more without leaving you feeling burnt out:

- Recovery should be founded, as much as possible, on doing the things that work for you; things that are enjoyable.
- It can be tempting to drop one or more of the activities that you do as part of your rehab – but be mindful

that the less you do, the more your mood is going to drop.

- You need to manage your fatigue levels, so start slowly. Don't over-pace yourself.
- Whenever possible, include family or friends in your recovery, so that they can help you stay on track when you are feeling less motivated.
- Establish a timetable for your week so that your regular activities start to become habitual.

Part III

The rehab team

Katherine Dawson

Introduction

In this section, we describe the roles of the chartered physiotherapist and the occupational therapist. They will describe the kind of work that they do and give you some examples of how they worked with Karl.

Of course, every practitioner has their own ways of working, but this will give you a broad-brush sense of their roles and responsibilities.

We have also included an introductory guide to the vestibular system to help you understand the role it plays in helping us balance – and the implications for what happens when it goes wrong.

Chapter 4

The chartered physiotherapist

Nicola Hunt

I start off with an assessment, which I split into two sessions on different days. The assessment process is such a tiring, physical process for the client to do in one go, and fatigue can affect the assessment results if the assessment is completed all in one session. This is the formal assessment process; however, assessment and re-assessment will be ongoing throughout the therapeutic relationship.

In the first assessment, I will get an idea of exactly what has happened and where the client has got to in the rehab journey. By this time, I will usually have had an initial needs assessment from the case manager, and I may have had supplementary letters and scan results.

I like to start by getting the client's perspective on how recovery has gone up to that point and get a sense of what their goals are. Then, in the next session, we will break those goals down into realistic targets. It can be quite demoralising to have a goal that you can only start to reach in two (or more) years' time, so I will set plenty of achievements en route to those goals to keep them engaged in the process.

First steps

At first, Karl found it hard to accept the level of his functional disability, and it was often hard for him to appreciate just how far he had come in his recovery. He was comparing himself with how he wanted to be and how he had been pre-accident.

From a physio point of view though, Karl was very disciplined and very structured in how he approached his life. That meant that he was very engaged with the physio process. He had a set list of things to do and a set programme of when he needed to do them.

In the early days, when he was still struggling with his dizziness and light-headedness, we started off with a little bit more passive treatment, along with the vestibular exercises – just to give him a little more symptom relief. It is extremely tiring when you constantly feel you are on a ship and the world is wobbling from side-to-side!

I treated Karl with acupuncture for symptom relief. I think it is fair to say that he was not convinced it was going to work, but he was committed to giving it a try. Western-style acupuncture is an adaptation of the traditional Eastern form of acupuncture. It may be something that is recommended as part of your treatment. I should reassure you that it is evidence based and supported by research for many conditions. In Karl's case, I used a standard dizziness post-traumatic brain injury protocol to help with his symptoms. If this form of treatment is appropriate for you, your chartered physiotherapist will recommend the most suitable treatment protocols to help.

Physical recovery

During our initial tests, we are assessing many aspects of physical ability, one of which is muscle strength, to see if the person has full power through full range (or available range) of movement. At my initial assessment of Karl, I found that his muscle tone was normal, power and isolated muscle testing also showed normal results, except for Karl's right hand, and grip in both hands. We have to be careful though because what we see when we carry out isolated muscle testing can be deceptive. For example, if I say "Straighten your knee," and you can do it, that does not necessarily correlate to going up a flight of stairs. It is not the same as doing it thirteen times with your full body weight on it. On objective power testing, Karl was fine. But that did not mean there were no functional problems.

When I first assessed him, Karl's grip strength was decreased on both sides. He had reduced movement at his shoulder, due to the orthopaedic injuries, and he had a lot of shortening of soft tissue, giving him a lack of flexibility, partly as a result of having been fairly immobile after a major injury. Testing showed he was significantly less dexterous than you would expect of someone of his age and certainly of someone whose job had required such great manual dexterity.

His balance was significantly reduced, due in part to reduced proprioception from his muscles and joints. As a result, he was over-reliant on his vision to stay balanced. We carry out different tests in different positions and on different surfaces, first with eyes open, and then with eyes closed to assess the different balance systems, vestibular, proprioception and vision.

In brain injuries, a vestibular problem is often central, so although the inner ear mechanism (vestibular system) remains intact, you need to be able to interpret the information from it, along with visual and proprioceptive information to determine where you are in space, and where to position your body for balance. Karl did not have a peripheral vestibular problem, he had central vestibular hypofunction, and his static balance tests showed just how visually reliant he was. When we took away vision (eyes closed) on either hard or foam surface, there was a reduction in balance and more so when we reduced proprioception. So the vestibular system was not functioning correctly.

We did a lot of retraining of balance, gait stability and saccadic eye movements and gaze stability to help Karl do some of the activities he had done before the accident without dizziness. This was particularly important for him to be able to resume his interest in photography, so he could scan through a camera lens, without losing focus.

There may also be an element of adaptation – you learn to live with (and compensate for) the difficulties. But it is important for us to work on and improve functioning as much as we can, to retrain the brain so its response to the stimulus does not result in dizziness.

We worked on various aspects of Karl's movement, looking at his ability to rise from sitting to standing, and then descend from standing to sitting. This gave us a good sense of what we call functional muscle power. This involves repetition of getting up and down from a chair and seeing how quickly you can do that. We use a standardised height chair, and we ask the client to sit and stand repeatedly, while timing them. This is a simple assessment of a functional activity and gives a marker for showing improvement.

I felt that Karl was very self-conscious about his injuries and the way he was perceived by others. One of his early goals was to improve his walking, but he went through a stage when he became very isolated and withdrawn in his house, and that compromised what physical rehab we could do. He was adamant that he would not go to a gym. To deal with this, we got a personal trainer to come and walk with him outside. This was to try and build up Karl's confidence to enable him to do it on his own and make it a part of his weekly routine. Of course, Karl being Karl, he went out for a walk a few days before the personal trainer was due to arrive! It did not matter, the suggestion of bringing in the personal trainer served its purpose. Karl was certainly very determined in that way. If you set him a challenge, he would want to beat you to it. That was always really nice to see.

I saw Karl from March 2016 and discharged him in October 2017, with an option of further treatment at any point in the future, should he feel he needs it. There is not always a clear cut-off point for treatment – most people can always go on improving. We need to try and assess the level at which you are comfortable stopping. When you are at (or nearing) that stage, your chartered physiotherapist will talk to you to discuss your goals and assess the progress you have made in meeting them. When I got to that point with Karl, he himself had come to the realisation that some of the goals he had set himself had not been that realistic, but he felt that he could continue to improve by continuing to do more of the things that we had been working on.

It must have been a difficult moment for Karl – to realise that there were some things that he just was not going to be able to do. He knew he had limitations. That is why Katherine's work with him was so important in helping him to be kinder to himself and in helping him recognise the achievements he had made in all areas of his recovery.

You will probably get to a point in your recovery, of rehab fatigue, the sense that rehab is endless and progress may feel slow, but your rehab team will work with you to find ways to keep things as interesting for you as possible.

In Karl's case, we got him started on indoor climbing. It met all the important goals for concentration, improving general strength, upper limb strength and coordination, and it was a perfect vehicle for his rehab. It was a whole new challenge for him, and he was really able to immerse himself in it. Having never done any climbing before, he did not have any self-imposed standards of expectation to measure himself against. Karl went from doing it as a part of his rehab, to doing it as an activity in its own right. When a friend visited him from America, he was able to take him climbing. That was a really nice point in his recovery. It gave him the sense of being the expert at something and teaching his friend what to do.

Helping someone to really engage with the recovery process is often about finding that motivation – something that really fires their imagination. You might be able to achieve the same physical results by staying in your room doing three sets of thirty squats, or you can go on a climbing wall and climb until your legs start shaking. They both have the same aim, but one is a little more fun than the other. Particularly after a brain injury, it is a long journey, and it is our job as therapists to try and make recovery functional and fun.

We always knew when we were on the right path with Karl whenever he took ownership of something. As well as the climbing, he really took to walking. Rather than me suggesting where he should walk to, he would plan a route on his computer and track the data about his time and distance. It is always lovely to see somebody take ownership of their rehab in that way.

I was certainly happy that Karl was ready to be discharged. We always do it on the proviso that, if you want to restart physio, you can. Along the way, there were times when I needed to remind him just how much progress he had made – and that is perhaps easier with physical rehab than it is in psychological or functional rehab because there are very clear markers of performance.

A traumatic brain injury changes your life. But your mission is not to try and recreate the life you had before, it is to try and create a new life for you that works. You may need to accept that there will be grieving for what you have let go, but that does not mean there will not be new achievements in the future, new experiences and new things that will bring joy to your life.

Chapter 5

The vestibular system explained

Nicola Hunt

The vestibular system is one of the three systems in our body, and the most important one, that help us to stay balanced. The other two systems are vision, and proprioception (information from our skin, muscles and joints).

The vestibular system is composed of several structures, but the main parts are three semi-circular canals in each inner ear, which are filled with a fluid and lined with tiny hairs. (Figure 5.1) They are at right angles to each other, to detect movement in different directions. In simple terms, when the head moves, the fluid moves the hairs, which leads to a message being passed to the brain about the movement.

Vision gives us clues as to our orientation. When we are upright and look at our surroundings, everything looks the 'right way up,' the way we are used to seeing it when we are upright. If we were to enter a room and all the furniture was on its side and the television picture was sideways, the visual message would be that we were lying on our side, but our vestibular system and vision give information to correct this message.

Proprioception is information from the skin, muscle and joints in response to stretch or pressure. Two specific areas that give us a lot of proprioceptive information are

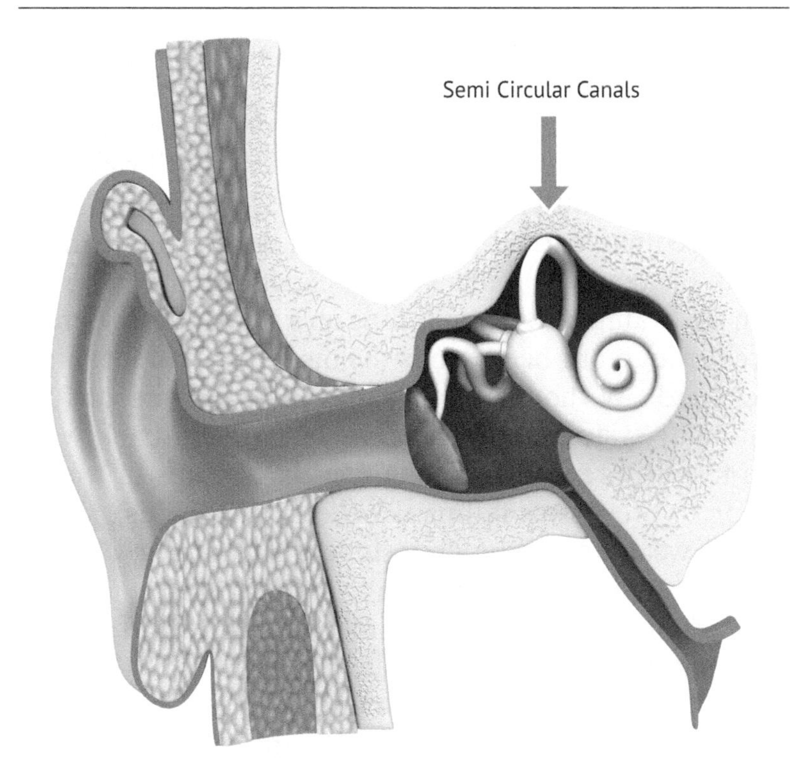

Figure 5.1 Semi-circular canals

the sensors in the neck and in the ankles. For example, when we stand, our ankles are at a right angle and the pressure on the sole of the foot fairly equal throughout the foot. When we lean forward, the pressure on the ball of the foot increases, and there is a stretch in the calf, giving information to the brain that we have leant forward. If we lean backwards, there is a change in the ankle joint position and more pressure on the heel of the foot. But what if we are standing on a slope? There is then more pressure on the heel of the foot, giving the message we are leaning backwards, but our vestibular system and vision give information to correct this message: we are upright but standing on a slope.

Knowing what position we are in, and what position we are in relative to our surroundings is important for movement. The angle we hold our cup of tea is dependent on our position, so that we hold it at one angle if we're sitting up, and a different angle if we are lying on the sofa. If we are unable to tell what position we are in, having a cup of tea could be quite a messy experience!

In the example above, standing on a slope with the pressure through our heels sends the message we are leaning backwards. Without any correcting information from the vestibular system and vision, we would step back with one foot to prevent us falling over backwards (a useful action to prevent us falling if we lean backwards). However, if we are standing on a slope we want to get to the top of, stepping backwards isn't very helpful.

So when we get conflicting information, it is often the information from the vestibular system that casts the deciding vote. Conflicting information can feel quite disorientating. Sitting on a stationary train next to one that suddenly starts to pull away can give you the sensation that you are moving. There is a brief period of feeling disorientated. The scenery is moving (visual message) but you are sitting still (proprioception message), and the vestibular system casts the deciding vote (agrees with proprioception).

Sending sensory information to the brain

All three systems give this sensory information to the brain, where it is processed and combined with information the cerebellum has learnt – through repetition – about automatic movement, and the knowledge and thinking provided by the cerebral cortex.

For example, when we walk along a pavement, we do not have to think about it because the movement pattern for walking is firmly stored in our cerebellum (the coordination centre of the brain). So, when we want to walk, we access our 'walking blueprint' and are able to walk without thinking about how to take every step. This is in direct contrast to when we do anything for the first time. For example, if we start playing tennis, we have to concentrate and think about how we perform the sequence of movements. (To serve, do we throw the ball up in the air first or swing our racket back? We have to concentrate to make sure we get this right.)

The cerebral cortex contributes previously learnt knowledge and thinking to a situation. If we are walking along the pavement we walk along every day, but today we can see the pavement is icy, the thinking and knowledge part of the brain knows that ice is slippery, and that if we walk along it as we usually do, we might fall over. So, instead of our normal 'walking blueprint' we need to concentrate on our walking, and move differently, altering our stride length and speed, maybe putting our arms out to the side for balance.

When there is damage or dysfunction of the vestibular system, it is harder to access our different blueprints for movements, as the information going to the brain is distorted. This means that people living with vestibular symptoms may have to concentrate on every move they make, literally. This is very tiring, and fatigue is a common symptom of vestibular disorders. Moreover, if the brain is busy concentrating on how to move and stay balanced, it has less capacity to concentrate on other things; hence, tasks that require thinking can become much harder.

The vestibular system is also closely related to the clarity of our vision. A reflex, known as the vestibulo-occular reflex moves your eyes in the opposite direction at a matched speed to head movements. If you turn your head to the left, your eyes move reflexively to the right, so you remain looking at the same point. This is an important reflex for clarity of vision. When we move, our head makes tiny movements from side to side. If we were not able to move our eyes to keep our vision fixed on the same spot – our visual field – what we'd see would appear to be moving slightly or appear double (Figure 5.2). We can override this reflex, for example if we want to look in a certain direction, we turn our head and eyes in the same direction. But for other tasks, such as reading or using a computer or tablet, it is important that this reflex is working properly to prevent what we are looking at being out of focus with every movement of our head. It is common for this reflex to not work properly in vestibular disorders, making vision slightly out of focus and therefore making tasks that require visual concentration

Figure 5.2 Double vision

(e.g. reading) difficult or impossible. Living in a world that is slightly out of focus as you move around, increases the sense of disorientation, and trying to force everything into focus can lead to fatigue. Headaches are another common symptom. Retraining this reflex is an important part of vestibular rehabilitation, improving gaze stability so that the world comes back into focus as you move around in it. This can include retraining of smooth pursuit (the ability of the eyes to follow a moving object smoothly) and saccadic eye movement (the eyes moving from one point to another, to look at two distinct objects).

So, balance, which we take for granted is actually quite complex. When all three systems are working well, and the brain processes the information well, we have good balance, clear vision as we move around, and we can adjust our posture to keep our balance as we do different activities. However, things can go wrong.

What can go wrong with the vestibular system and balance?

There are many conditions and causes of vestibular disorders, which will not be included here. Following a head injury, anywhere from a mild traumatic brain injury (often called a concussion) up to a severe brain injury, vestibular problems are very common, and come under two categories: Peripheral problems (i.e. problems with the vestibular apparatus in the inner ear and the vestibular nerve) and central problems (problems with the way the brain receives and processes all the information). Following a brain injury, it is quite common to have both peripheral and central problems.

The most common peripheral problem following a traumatic brain injury is benign paroxysmal positional vertigo (BPPV). Benign means it is not life threatening; paroxysmal means it comes on suddenly for brief periods; positional means it is triggered by certain head movements or positions and vertigo means a false sense of rotational movement.

BPPV is caused by the crystals that are in a part of the vestibular apparatus becoming dislodged and moving into one or more of the semi-circular canals, where they are not meant to be. These crystals can interfere with the normal movement of the fluid and can trigger messages of movement to be sent, when no movement has occurred, or incorrect messages about the movement.

Central problems relate to the brain and the way it processes the vestibular information it receives. An injury to the brain, whether structural, that shows up on a scan, or functional, as is the case with a mild traumatic brain injury (or concussion) can affect the areas that process vestibular information and enable us to balance.

So how does it feel when balance, and in particular the vestibular system goes wrong?

Think of the feeling of disorientation we experience as the train next to our train pulls away and we have conflicting information to process. Now consider how much worse that would be if the vestibular system couldn't give the casting vote. Or worse still, the information from the left vestibular apparatus didn't match the information from the right vestibular apparatus.

As we move our head independently of anything else (as in nodding) or our whole self, including our head (as in walking) then the message from each ear would be the same. However, if on one side of the vestibular apparatus was not working properly, the message from each side would be different. One side would be giving the correct information, the other side could be sending quite a different message, or no message at all. If one inner ear is sending information that you are walking forwards and the other inner ear is not sending any message about movement, essentially telling the brain you are still, it is easy to understand that disorientation and dizziness is the outcome.

Think back to your childhood and being on a roundabout or spinning round and round. When you spin, you are moving the fluid in the semi-circular canals of your vestibular apparatus. When you stop, the fluid takes a little longer to come to a stop as it has gathered momentum with the repeated spinning. But as soon as you stop, your proprioception and vision send the message you have stopped. The message from the vestibular system, the most significant system of balance, causes the disorientation and you feel dizzy, and maybe slightly nauseous, until the fluid comes to rest and the dizziness stops.

Try walking in a straight line when feeling like this. It is impossible, and you would stagger like you were drunk. Now that's fine when you are eight and have just come off the roundabout. No one judges you. But what happens when you are an adult trying to do your shopping in town at 9.30 in the morning? Feeling the stares of other people and their judgements that you are drunk.

Try to fill in some complicated form whilst feeling like this. How well do you think you would be able to concentrate, or get the details right?

Vestibular disorders can feel like this all the time, or on any movement of the head, or on specific movements. Each and every person will experience the symptoms slightly differently, but in general this mismatch in information results in the symptoms of dizziness, vertigo, vision problems, nausea, sometimes vomiting, fatigue and concentration difficulties that people with vestibular problems can experience.

A vestibular physiotherapist can complete an assessment, which includes a variety of different tests, to determine the cause of the dizziness and prescribe and deliver an individual course of treatment. In some cases, this will completely resolve the problem, such as in BPPV. In other cases it retrains the brain and body to reduce or eliminate dizziness and other symptoms and improve the balance and regain function. Vestibular rehabilitation commonly includes gaze stability exercises to improve control of eye movements, so that vision remains clear when the head is moved, and personalised exercises and balance retraining. You can expect that in addition to the sessions with your chartered physiotherapist, you will be prescribed some exercises and activities to continue on your own between sessions. These will be suitable for your level of symptoms, ensuring you are able to complete them safely.

In the case of BPPV, repositioning manoeuvres can be performed to move the crystals out of the semi-circular canals. These manoeuvres must be performed by a suitably trained chartered physiotherapist, or other suitably trained health care professional.

Chapter 6

The occupational therapist

Louise Watkins

As an occupational therapist (OT), I am concerned with the many and varied ways in which a client's condition affects their day-to-day living. Of course, everybody has a different lifestyle and different priorities, so it is important to identify what each person's interests and goals are as part of the rehabilitation process. I look holistically to promote independence, meaningful occupations, and to restore functional ability. The ultimate aim is to fulfil the client's potential to engage in activities related to their daily living, including vocational roles.

I met Karl in March 2016, while he was still living on the RAF base. He had just started a graded return to work. The first time I saw him, he was lying on his bed, wearing casual clothes. He told me that he would never have met me in those clothes before the accident, as he had been very fashion conscious, and enjoyed purchasing designer clothes. He explained that the physical effort of dressing in his usual smart clothes was too demanding and exacerbated his fatigue. This was just one example of the impact the accident had upon his personal identity.

Whilst Karl had returned to work, he had no capacity to do anything else, physically, cognitively and emotionally; he was burnt out. He was living in one small room, with no cooking facilities except for a microwave. He did go out when he had to, if only to buy food, but it was hard for him, and his reliance on quick microwave meals was compromising his nutritional intake. He went to sleep with the TV playing constantly, so his sleep hygiene was also very poor. At that time, Karl was really just existing. He had no physical or cognitive reserve left to engage with any other aspects of life.

Recognising that work was having such a negative impact on his well-being and participation in other aspects of daily living, Karl was signed off as unfit for work. This was a catalyst to move off the base and into a bungalow. Karl found the practicalities of independent living – like having to cook and clean – quite overwhelming. With Amy's help, we put a list of jobs together to help him. Although it's true that Amy's and my expectations may have been a little optimistic, and we all had some laughs about that! But really, this was less about the standards of cleaning and more about giving him a greater sense of control over his routine. Just having that little bit of guidance and structure helped him, and Karl still uses lists and timetables to help him manage his times and activities.

We looked at his pre-morbid lifestyle and leisure activities, particularly his interest in photography, cars and bikes. As he put it, he just wanted to get some of that life back and get to the point where he had more energy to be able to do what he described as 'normal things'. For him, this meant simple things like being able to dress in the clothes he wanted to wear and being able to shave without difficulty again. Underpinning all of this, the most significant barrier for him was fatigue.

We looked at the principles of fatigue management, and in particular, pacing and grading activities. One of an OT's core skills is problem-solving and specifically trying to find different ways of doing things to help clients readjust to their new situation. The challenge with Karl was getting him to accept the necessity to do things in a different way from how he had done them before his accident. Karl had previously described himself as 'King Karl'. His stance was: "If I can't do it the way I did it before, I'm not going to do it." This is how people can get stuck in their recovery. If you are not going to even try to do things differently, you either become less independent, or you have to consider doing those things in an adapted way.

This is where the strength of the team comes into play. Katherine worked with Karl to find different strategies for helping him to become more independent – and yes, he hated that word 'strategies!' Initially, we needed to take his rehabilitation at a slower pace, to take into account the significant mental adjustment required. This understanding of Karl's barriers had to underpin everything that I did if I was going to help him on that journey to greater acceptance.

Another one of Karl's priorities had been to get back to photography, but he felt it would be impossible. He did not even think he had the strength and stamina to carry his kit. We did some work around how we could lessen his burden, including choosing one standard lens for the photos he wanted to take, rather than taking a selection. We worked on the best ways to carry his camera and tripod, and we went to Whisby Nature Reserve. The compromise of not taking as much gear was worth it, as it showed him that he could still do some of what he wanted to do. I needed Karl to be able to succeed and graded the activity to suit his capability. That meant taking every last detail into account; choosing a nearby location with good parking and good spots for photography that were easily accessible. One successful trip led to another and that gave him the confidence to return to Cadwell Park to photograph the motorbikes – something else he thought he had lost. Preparation for that activity involved several team members and was co-ordinated by the case manager. This is a further example of how everyone works together to achieve a set goal.

Such activities gave Karl the opportunity to drive more and further afield. When I met him, Karl had already passed the test to confirm he was still safe to drive after the accident but had not driven very much. In order for him to be confident and able to get to Cadwell Park, he followed me in his car to Hull. That was an adapted strategy to help re-familiarise him with routes, and it helped him regain some of that lost confidence. Nicola had also done some vestigial work with him to help him process things more easily when he was in the car. Then, when he went to Cadwell the first time, he went with Amy. So, between us all, we covered different elements of the task.

As described earlier in this book, Karl decided to go to America. When somebody has only just started to travel independently, it was a big test of their independent ability. Working with his case manager, we did a risk assessment. Karl was physically up to the task of going, but we needed to consider the mental stimulation that would hit him in the airport. We arranged some additional assistance at the airport to guide him through and onto the plane. Because Karl was so motivated to go to America, he recognised where he needed to accept additional support.

*

A large part of my role is about showing people what they *can* do. As part of that process with Karl, I was very aware of how socially isolated he was. This is a common problem. When you are part of a work group, you are usually part of a team. When you are no longer in that environment you end up spending a lot more time alone, and this can negatively affect your mood.

Addressing this issue and Karl's goal of wanting to explore vocational rehabilitation, I suggested Hill Holt Wood. Hill Holt is a social enterprise that operates within the community to provide a range of services, including forestry management and education courses in the woodland. Karl grudgingly conceded that he would go and give it a try, but, as he said, "only because I trust you."

With all of these things, it is important to take the stress out of the situation, so I suggested to Karl that we would only go to take a look. It would be left up to him to decide if he went back. But Karl loved it and he made some very good friends there too.

The physical work he did at Hill Holt was obviously very important for his ongoing physical recovery. And, as we were looking at return to work options, we got him involved in the administrative side of things to help him problem solve and project manage things.

I accompanied Karl when he went back to work. One of the keys skills of an OT is to assist and empower clients to overcome obstacles to their return to work, or else transfer their skills to other meaningful occupations. We did a lot of preparation around his work role and considered what he might be capable of doing.

If you are in the position of preparing to return to work, your OT should be able to support a vocational rehabilitation plan which will probably involve liaising with your employer and occupational health team. Where possible there will be a work site visit to enable the OT to assess the tasks and processes involved throughout a job, and analyse the demands this may have on the client completing the work role. This informs a rehabilitation plan that will help you and highlight any reasonable adjustments required.

The key is grading your return to work and helping you to return to as similar a job as possible, in the right way. For some people returning to work in a different capacity is an acceptable compromise. In Karl's case, we knew that both cognitively and physically, he would not have been able to do what he had done before. That was difficult for him, but he did not really know how difficult it was going to be until he had the opportunity to try. As a result, it became clear that we needed to consider what the rehab team calls a positive exit, in which the employee, knowing that their ability has been too severely compromised, takes the decision to leave for themselves. Again, having some element of autonomy and control is really important.

Karl was subsequently medically retired. At an earlier point in his rehabilitation, that would have been a bitter blow, but by this stage, Karl was much more positive. We talked about the transition into a different looking life and how that was going to work for him. Karl was far too bright and creative to waste away at home, doing nothing. Throughout the time we spent together, Karl really increased his awareness (and acceptance) of his strengths and weaknesses. That left him much more able to consider different options for his future.

A big part of the job we do as a team is preparing clients to be as independent as possible. Karl exemplifies this: he is now functioning independently, and emotionally, he has come a long way. To some degree, he has learnt to accept where he is in his life now. The rehabilitation process – in all aspects – has empowered him to live again.

Part IV

Community-based rehab

Katherine Dawson

Introduction

Ash was referred to our service by his rehab medicine consultant in the NHS.

Ash was a bright, articulate, intelligent man who was engaged to be married. Life was full of promise and then he was involved in a terrible accident. Knocked off his motorcycle, Ash's injuries were so severe that his family was told he only had a 20% chance of survival, and he could be dead within the week. But Ash was strong and pulled through.

When I got involved, Ash had been discharged home with a care package in place, but the agency staff were struggling to get Ash engaged in functionally meaningful activity to continue his rehab. He was low in mood, not eating, and spending a lot of time in bed. Ash's consultant asked us to assess Ash with a view to putting some intensive rehab assistant sessions in place in the community. It was clear that his family also wanted Ash to have greater structure to his day and to engage in meaningful activity to help him go on to increase his independence.

I had received details of Ash's brain injury following a motorbike accident, and the scans revealed a large blood clot and swelling of his brain, as well as skull fractures and multiple bruising throughout. This led to a diagnosis of an extremely severe traumatic brain injury. As part of the assessment process, I met with Ash to complete some paper and pencil testing to help identify what he could do well, and what areas he was struggling with. My role in this case, due to the limits on funding, focussed on developing a rehab programme for our rehab assistants to deliver in the community.

After the assessment, my role also focussed on supporting the family with managing Ash's behaviours. We met to brainstorm what some of the brain injury and non–brain-injury-related barriers were to his rehab. Based on the nature of his accident and the scan results, it was clear that the significant damage to the front part of the brain affected aspects of Ash's attention and concentration, his emotions and fatigue. Ash would often get stuck in a loop verbally and find it difficult to switch off his thoughts. He also found it difficult to stay 'online' with an activity for a long period of time. Consequently, his brain would tire easily and when this happened, he could become agitated. He also found it difficult to find the right word, which caused him understandable frustration. Finally, and one of the most hidden difficulties was his reduced motivation. Ash's brain found it much more difficult to kick-start activity, and consequently, he spent a lot of time in bed when we initially got involved, feeling unmotivated and unable to do anything. We discussed needing to focus on activities that would bypass the effortful part of the process as a priority to help him regain his motivation.

I also developed behavioural guidelines (which were basically scripted responses that took into account the nature of Ash's brain injury, but also considered who he was as a person) to help others respond to Ash when he was getting agitated. We talked a lot about naming his emotions and giving him the opportunity to express his frustration. We linked this to use of reminiscence, so when he was describing how much he missed his fiancé, Gladys, we would ask him to tell us about how he had met her. And when he was frustrated that he couldn't get out and about, we would ask him to tell us about where he had travelled before. We also spent time talking about how to respond when Ash became agitated and struggled to reason.

In order to help Ash kick start his brain, we identified rehab activities that had a very meaningful focus. Tim, our rehab assistant, had spent time with Ash and his family and had identified that Ash had interests in: walks and looking at wildlife, classic cars and shadow boxing.

As a team, we want rehab to tackle the strong sense of loss people experience around: their role and identity, changes to relationships, reduced communication and social skills and isolation and difficulties understanding and coping with social situations.

Working alongside Olivia – another one of our rehab assistants – and the support team, Tim focussed on increasing the structure in Ash's week, and they developed a local resource file to identify appropriate community-based activities. We agreed rehab activities would be split into the following:

1. Physical rehab, with a focus on incorporating all of the physical recommendations made by Ash's physio into more functional activities. Ash had difficulties starting tasks (due to his significant frontal lobe damage) so we proposed that one rehab session a week would focus

on a shadow boxing activity. The aims were twofold: to tap into his sense of identity and self-worth but also to allow development of a routine that could be handed over to the support team, promoting ongoing functional movement, physical activity and a degree of cardiovascular exercise.

2. A social activity, and we began with funding dance classes for Ash who wanted to surprise his fiancée with a dance routine when she came home at Christmas! Tim talks in more detail about how Ash responded to the activities and the benefits of a more structured approach to rehab a little later on.

In this section, we will look at Ash's story with contributions from Ash; his niece (and carer/personal assistant) Sameera: his fiancé, Gladys, and his rehab assistant, Tim.

Chapter 7

Ash's story

Ashraf Sheikh and Sameera Sheikh

For so long, Ash (or Lali Mamu as his family know him) was the head of the household. A clever, strong and family-oriented man, he helped raise his two nieces and brought money into the family from his work around the world. He worked in security in Uganda, he supplied close protection services to the Kenyan government and he worked on door security in the UK. He certainly knew how to handle himself in a fight, but Ash was possessed of the sort of inner strength that meant he never had to throw his weight around. He commanded respect, love and admiration – and thanks to his incredible recovery, he still does...

Ash is modest about his achievements and about the dangerous life he's lived. "In Kenya, a lot of people wanted to kill politicians. It was my job to look after them. But to do that, I couldn't be the aggressor; I didn't want to shoot people. I had to show them that I had the means to kill them and give them the opportunity to put down their weapon. Not all of my colleagues were like that. I was in a lot of dangerous situations. I worked in Kenya for three years, and there were a lot of people who could have killed me. I saw them almost every day. But I knew what I was doing, and people could see that I meant business. It helped avoid a lot of bloodshed."

Ash had a busy life, splitting his time between different places, but always caring for his family, and looking after the people closest to him, including the woman he is going to marry, Gladys. She says, "We met in March 2016. A mutual friend introduced us, at a party held by a social expatriate's club, and it was attraction at first sight. I could see straightaway that Ash was a cheerful, happy guy. In time, and as I got to know him better, I realised that he also was a strong-minded person, determined and quite stubborn ... but he never lost his kind, sweet manners with me."

Ash and Gladys fell in love, and Ash divided his time between the UK and Kenya. But on his visit to Kenya in December 2017, their lives were torn apart. Gladys explains, "We had made so many plans for his stay in Nairobi, there was going to be Christmas together and my birthday in January. The day before the accident, we attended a gala party. It was an amazing night for us; Ash was over the moon with his happiness, and so was I. The next day he left home while I was getting ready; we were going to visit his mum, and he wanted to take her samosas..."

Ash tell us what he remembers, "I was going to get my mum's favourite food for her. I called out to Gladys that I'd be back in a minute. That's the last thing I remember of my old life ... I know I was on a big motorcycle, and the car just smashed into me. I do remember thinking: *this is the end.* I wasn't wearing a crash helmet. You don't have to wear them in Kenya. I think I heard someone say 'He won't make it past three days.'"

Gladys continues, "Twenty minutes later, a friend called and told me that Ash had had an accident and was in a critical condition. At first, I could not believe it; on my way to the hospital I was praying for it to be a mistake. All I could do was ask God to please keep him alive. When I saw him in front of me, bathed in blood, and fighting with the doctors and nurses to get up and leave, my heart sank, and it was in that moment that I understood that he needed to hear my voice to help him calm down. I knew that I had to be strong for him – it was the best way I could help him."

Ash had eight broken ribs, a broken clavicle and a punctured lung. There was considerable brain damage. But he was strong. Three days passed – three days he had not been expected to survive – and although his condition remained critical, he slowly started to improve.

"I was in the hospital in Kenya for a few days, and Gladys was there to look after me. And then my sisters, Ruby, Tamsy and Neela, arranged to fly me back to England. I was brought to Hull Royal, and they fixed me up really well."

Ash's niece, Sameera, takes up the story, "Gladys had such a terrible experience, she was the one who saw him covered in blood, unable to move, and seemingly hours from death. She saw him through those first few days when no one knew if he would live or die. By the time he was brought back to Hull Royal, three weeks after the crash, he had lost a lot of weight and looked like a different person. It was so hard in those first few weeks after the crash. We still didn't know if he was going to pull through."

"I was talking to a neighbour about what had happened, and she told me about her daughter's husband. He had been out on his bike and was involved in a terrible crash. Lali Mamu had been in a crash without a crash helmet or any protective clothing and survived, whereas this man, who couldn't have been any better protected, had died. And that's when I knew how lucky we had been."

"He was in intensive care at Hull Royal for three weeks, on life support, and fully sedated, to give his body the chance to start healing. He was in quarantine too. He'd picked something up in the hospital in Kenya. The feeding tube they'd been using was contaminated. So he was on industrial-strength antibiotics for that. Then, in January 2018, he was moved to the infectious diseases unit, where he was slowly brought back to full consciousness." Ash began to converse slowly in the different languages he was fluent in before the accident. Sameera says, "I am so proud of Lali Mamu, that he can switch from English to Spanish, then from Punjabi/Urdu to Swahili; we were told he wouldn't ever be able to speak properly again."

At that time, one of the hardest prospects for Gladys, Sameera and the family to deal with was the possibility that when he came out of his coma, Ash wouldn't remember them. Gladys says "That was my worst fear – would he even know me when he woke up? I kept talking to him all the time when he was still in the hospital in Nairobi. But it was hard when he was brought to the UK; I couldn't speak to him anymore, and I was so scared of what could happen when he opened his eyes. I read so many articles about brain injury and the long-term impact it can have, and I had many scary moments and sleepless nights worrying about what might happen."

"At the beginning he didn't remember exactly who I was, but it wasn't long before he was showing me his love for me, just like he had before. He still wasn't talking, or showing complete recognition of everyone, but he always calmed down when he heard my voice."

"I made a book of memories for him with pictures from our times together in Nairobi. Sometimes, when we are looking at the book together, he tells me that he does not remember those days and when I ask him 'And how do you love me so much then?' His answer is 'I don't know, darling. I just feel that I love you with all my heart.' I have kept constant daily communication with Ash ever since he started to talk again. We speak on the phone every day, sometimes two, three and even four times a day. We listen to each other and share daily life experiences. I keep him updated about what is going on in my life, and he talks to mutual friends in Kenya when I am with them. I talk to him about my family, my sons and my grandchildren. It is a constant exchange of daily life experiences, albeit 7,000 kilometres away. Most importantly of all, I listen to him. It's important that he knows he can tell me about his happiness and his frustrations."

And there *have* been frustrations, particularly early in the process. Sameera explained that there were times when the enormity of what had happened to him was still quite difficult for Ash to deal with. "I haven't had any experience in dealing with significant cognitive issues. So it hasn't always been easy to manage him when he has been moody or upset. Because of his brain injury, we don't know how he will react sometimes. He can get a bit moody. And that can be hard to deal with. I tend to just leave him until he's calmed down, and then we go from there."

The family worked hard to give Ash the supportive environment he needed to feel safe to express his frustrations and his difficulties. And Ash's own resolve to make the most of his life after the crash was a huge factor. The critical thing for everyone to remember was simply that these things take time. Healing is an up-and-down road that is full of surprises!

There was still a lot of physical rehabilitation to be done too. Sameera says, "Lali Mamu came home in June 2018. That's when I stopped my work as a solicitor so that I could look after him. His carers had begun the process of his physical rehabilitation, but as time wore on, we could see that he really needed something to engage his enthusiasm. That's when we were introduced to our rehab assistant, Tim…"

*

Tim takes up the story, "I met Ash in the spring of 2019, and following a rehab assessment, we put together a proposal for a three-month support package for him and the family."

"Physically, Ash was in a wheelchair when I met him and couldn't walk long distances. His upper body was quite strong, but he was working with the physio to help him with improving the weakness on his left side."

"Cognitively, he was quite impaired. He was unable to engage with some of the assessments at that time, and was displaying some behavioural difficulties, which his family and support staff were struggling to manage. Because of the time post-injury, and the results of the testing Katherine completed, and Ash's difficulties with insight, we wanted to focus on activities that would give him the most enjoyment, and, physically, the things that would help him feel like he was making the most progress, aiming eventually to enhance his identity and self-worth."

"Ash had two rotating care staff at that time, as well as his family helping him out. They were all really supportive when it came to getting Ash out as much as possible, taking him out for walks, or to the shops. So we included all of them in our rehab plans."

"To begin with, I wanted to find out more about what he liked to do. At that stage, Ash wasn't verbalising very much, but Ash's family was very helpful in giving us ideas for activities that would be meaningful for him. And we knew from his background that he was a strong male figure in the family, whom everyone had always looked up to. He'd used to be a bouncer, and he had enjoyed going to the gym. Boxing training and table tennis both came up."

The boxing was a good fit for Ash. When he was ten years old, he met Muhammed Ali in Kenya, who made quite an impression. "He was huge!" Inspired by Ali's achievements, Ash started boxing. He thought that one day he might be able to knock out Muhammed Ali!

"We set up some boxing classes for him. I told the boxing coach what Ash's limiting factors were and outlined what we were working towards over the course of twelve weeks, in furthering Ash's confidence, mobility and dexterity. Obviously, there was no punching to the head, we concentrated on pushing and pulling, shadow boxing, pad work and work on the punch bag. Sameera and Ruby were in tears the first time they saw him in the ring; just seeing him do something active felt like a big step forward."

"It was a great work out for Ash. His heart rate went up, his breathing rate increased, he had to work hard. And it helped him feel the strength coming back to his body. Of course, we had to very carefully manage his fatigue levels. It can be exhausting at first to do any activity after so long being idle. So when Ash wanted to stop, we did."

Ash's enthusiasm about boxing was a real positive. Prior to this, he had been spending a lot of time in bed, and we understood this as a consequence of his difficulty kick-starting his brain, plus his low mood as a result of what he had been through.

"Ash was still very weak on the left side, so the coach adapted his activities to fit. Ash could feel himself getting better every week. And, at the end of the twelve weeks, it was clear to all of us (and especially the neuro-physio team) that there had been a massive improvement."

As the rehab progressed, we also began to see more of the fiercely independent side of Ash. There were times when he would get up and tell us he was going out. That might be for a walk around the block, or it might be a trip away for the weekend. He didn't always plan; he didn't want to feel constricted by those kinds of arrangements. This completely fitted his spontaneous lifestyle before the accident, and it was important that we understood this and bridged into his world, whilst identifying activities that would fit with his spontaneity but still had a certain structure.

"One thing that Ash wanted to be able to do was dance at his own wedding. So we arranged for some dance classes, and Ash completed three sessions so he could surprise his fiancée when she came over at Christmas. Whilst the complexity of the movements he had to master were challenging and Ash often found it difficult to inhibit moving freestyle to the music, he had identified a meaningful goal and he had tried it."

"We always have to be mindful of the fact that not every activity will work in the way we want. But we also have to be flexible enough to turn any disappointments into further opportunities for something positive... Ash had always enjoyed cycling, and the family had a couple of bikes that needed repairing. I do some work with a bicycle charity, so we arranged it for Ash to take the bikes there and work on them with a bike mechanic, one-to-one for one hour a week until the bikes were finished."

"As an activity, it ticked a lot of boxes. It was great test of hand–eye coordination and the dexterity between his fingers. He had to listen and act on what the mechanic was telling him and do his jobs in the right order. Over the weeks, we saw some significant improvements. But what we didn't foresee was Ash's disappointment; we had thought that the satisfaction of fixing the bikes for his family was his primary driver, but he had been hoping that, at the end of it, he would be able to ride the bike."

"When he found out that he wasn't going to be able to ride his own bike, it was difficult for Sameera and Ruby to deal with his disappointment as Ash's behaviour became quite challenging. We looked at an assisted riding scheme in Hull – where you ride side-by-side – and he tried that. Unfortunately, that still didn't satisfy his need to fix and ride his own bike."

"But even that apparent setback was a valuable learning curve for everyone. Because Ash took that disappointment and worked towards making himself able to have a go at riding his own bike again. And we gave him and the family some guidelines to help him do that and got the physio team to assess him for riding as well. In the end, Ash being Ash, just got on the bike one day and started riding it. Everyone was very scared, but he managed it."

"The big lesson in all of this is that you can't always successfully predict people's responses. For someone as strong-willed as Ash – and let's remember, that strength of character is a big part of what pulled him through – we couldn't know for certain, how he would take to any activity if he felt that it held him back in any way."

"Of course, managing expectations is a very important part of the whole rehab process. And sometimes, that means dealing with disappointment. Driving was a big loss for Ash; he even had a classic car in his garage that he loved and talked to us about all the time."

"Initially, we considered the same approach to the car as we'd taken with the bike – thinking Ash could work with a mechanic on the car to keep it in tip-top condition. But given the disappointment he'd felt with not being able to ride the bike, we held back. At that time, Ash still couldn't quite understand why he couldn't drive the car. And in those cases, it needs a professional, rather than a carer or family member, to explain exactly why a person isn't capable of doing something that they still feel like they can do."

"Most people will have something that they can't do anymore as a consequence of their injury. From a physical perspective it may be any of the following: walking up a flight of stairs, standing up out of a chair or taking themselves off to the toilet – any one of a number of things that we just take for granted. More hidden difficulties can include changes in thinking and memory and emotional control. So, all of these losses – of independence, of skills, of confidence, of ability – can feel overwhelming. That's why it's important for us to be positive about what you *can* do."

"Ash could still play table tennis. So we put a table up in his house. It didn't take long for me to see he was a really good table tennis player; he had plenty of skills. We did lots of rallies together, and he enjoyed playing with his family. We also recommended a local table tennis social group."

Ash is still weaker on his left side, where his clavicle broke. It means that walking remains a little bit more difficult, and his balance isn't what it was. And all of that means that everyday activities can be particularly tiring for him. But his strength has improved after his work with Tim, and he isn't discouraged, "I've only got one leg that isn't quite right. And I had a blister on my foot, which turned into a diabetic ulcer. But I'm nearly all done – nearly 100%."

Tim is full of respect for the work that Ash and his family put into the process. "When our time came to an end, it was important that we gave them as much support as possible. We recommended some local agencies to help them feel connected, and to help them to keep engaging Ash in activities. We also handed over a rehab timetable to support the family to continue with structured activities to help Ash to continue to learn by doing."

"The work that we did, and the support his family have given them, has helped Ash make some significant improvements. He gained so much from the activities he engaged in, and his family helped in that process enormously."

*

Psychologically, as well as physically, Ash is in a different place. "Now I can start again. I can get married to Gladys..."

The crash put all of Ash and Gladys's plans for the future on hold. "Our relationship came to a halt with Ash's accident," Gladys explains. "We had many plans together; he was planning to move permanently to Nairobi and wait for my retirement, which, at that time, was four years away. We had plans to buy a house in Spain and move there later and to go all around Europe in a caravan. We had even planned to get married in Mombasa on the south coast of Kenya."

Now, two years after the crash, they are planning their wedding again. And Ash is already thinking about the longer-term future ...

"We can go to Gladys's place in Malaga, Spain, and we can start a business. Lots of people out there want good Indian food, and I can cook it. I also know someone in Kenya, and he'd like me to come and work for him. So, my goal for the future is to get back to work. I'm going to look after my mum as well. She came back to the UK with my brother and lives in Leicester. She's eighty-six now, and I can look after her. Gladys is going to help me."

Sameera isn't surprised by her uncle's attitude, "He's always been that kind of person – making plans to look after his family. He was always there to protect us when we were growing up, and then, later in life, he would always come over and see us when he could. He always made sure the family was alright. Then perhaps he'd be off to London, or over to Europe – always with more plans for making money; it was a way of life he really enjoyed. So it's been hard for him, sitting stagnant, all that time. The thought of getting married, and going to Kenya, or over to Spain, has helped him cope. He has always been able to keep his spirit up."

Not being used to be in one place for so long, Ash has had quite an adjustment to make to life in recuperation. And that has been hard for everyone to deal with. Sameera says, "There have been times when he's got frustrated, not so much with the pace of recovery, but with the loss of independence he has had." At times, Ash has felt that frustration very keenly, but says, "That's my focus now – getting more independent." That independence is within Ash's reach; early in 2020, he is due for an independent living assessment to ensure he is able to carry out basic tasks for himself, and look after himself.

It has been a long and difficult road to where Ash is now. "After the accident, I really thought there was nothing left. I thought I was as good as dead. So when I started to get better, I felt so happy to just still be alive. Now, I am looking forward to getting married and trying new things. I have had so much support to help me through this – from Gladys and my family. A smash like I had could have been the end, but as soon as I started to get over it, I just wanted to get on with living my life again. I just had to get on with it – and that's what I'm doing now."

Sameera explains, "He had that mindset before the accident as well. He was always a get-up-and-do-it kind of a guy. And we all had to work together on his recovery." There wasn't any funding for some of the support that the family would have liked, but Sameera believes that, "There is a lot that you as a loving family member can do to support someone. It can be difficult at times. There are bad things as well as good. This is the man who practically brought me up from the age of four, so that makes for a different dynamic. When his carers went, I think Lali Mamu thought he was fine, so we had to deal with that too. And I had to make sure he kept on working on all of his strategies."

"But he is still very much the same person. He still has those strengths that I remember from when we were kids. He is still very particular about things, still very enthusiastic about getting things done and still very caring. What has changed is that realisation that he isn't as strong as he used to be, and that he isn't able to do everything he did before."

Ash knows that he will never be able to ride a motorbike again, and, at the time of writing, he is still unable to drive a car, his balance isn't yet good enough. He's been riding a motorbike in Kenya since he was just ten years old and knowing that he'll never be able to ride again has been hard for him to deal with. It signalled a loss of independence he has always prized so highly.

Sameera says, "The injury to his foot has stopped him regaining his independence quite as quickly as he would have liked – and that is frustrating for him too. Before, he might have dealt with his frustrations by getting out on his bike. Then he would come back feeling happier. But now, he doesn't have that opportunity. Now, he has to deal with what he's feeling – and I don't think he ever really had to do that before. He was always moving on to the next thing. So I think that he has had to deal with a lot more frustration, but as a result, he has learnt to become a little bit more patient. And we have had to learn to give him that space and that patience he needs."

Ash explains, "When I get frustrated, I have to think about the future. At the moment, I am thinking about going to Kenya, and that is what we're planning for now." And Sameera agrees, "Anyone in this situation has to have that focus. I think they key for Lali Mamu has been having that end goal: he wants to go to Kenya, he wants to get his independence back; he wants to get married and to buy a house with Gladys in Spain. He hasn't let the enormity of what happened to him stop him from thinking about the future. He is always focussed on what he's going to do next. He's always been very practical and forward-focussed. Sometimes it's his sheer stubbornness that has helped pull him through! That's allowed him to achieve so much in his recovery in such a short space of time. At the beginning we didn't even know if he was going to be able to walk again."

"He is still making improvements. His memory isn't what it was; the last twenty years are very hazy for him. For example, when we celebrated his birthday last year, he was convinced he was thirty – not fifty. He remembers us girls being four and five. That has been quite hard for the people who love him to deal with. It sounds silly to say, but he's the kind of guy who you never thought this would happen to. He was always so strong. From a child's perspective, he always seemed invincible. And it was hard to see that deterioration …

"But his love for his family is still so strong, and you still feel that, even though there is twenty years missing. And you can still see his strength in the way he has rebuilt his life. That stubbornness has helped pull him through."

Sameera knows that his memories are all still there. "Songs and photographs can instantly trigger some of those memories to come back. Very often he'll pick up a song, and it'll take him back to something that happened. The memories are all in there, it just takes little triggers to bring them out. It's interesting for me too. There are lots of things about Lali Mamu's life that I didn't know. He kept his personal life very personal. So now I'm finding out all sorts of things I never knew about him."

Making the most of life

Ash remains positive, "Even if you think it is the end, what has happened to you makes you look at things differently. Even if your life is going to be different, you can still make something of that other life. You can't just stop. You can't just give up and say it's finished. You have to carry on."

"Thank God I'm so stubborn. It's helped me. And maybe the smash helped me see things differently – it made me think *you have to do other things – you can't die like this. You have your family* ... I knew there was more to live for."

"I'm so grateful to Sameera and the whole family – they tell me that things will carry on; things will get better. I used to look after Sameera when she was small, and now she's looking after me." Sameera adds, "The difference is he used to pick me up and throw me in the air – I could never throw him in the air! He's too big!"

It's telling that when Ash woke up properly for the first time after the crash, the first thing he thought of was his family. Sameera says, "Straightaway he was asking after his mum, Gladys, my mum and my sister. He just wanted to know that everyone was alright." Sameera knows that was one of the factors in his recovery. He knew he had to get better so he could look after everyone again.

"When we were growing up and we would be worried about exams, and I would tell him, I can't do it. And Lali Mamu would say to me, what do you mean, 'can't'? We weren't allowed to use the word 'can't' – and he's applied that same thinking to his own recovery. So even when things have been hard, and he's really been struggling, he's always maintained that he can do it."

No one knows what the future holds, and everyone appreciates that there are still difficult times ahead. Gladys says, "Ash's brain injury is quite serious. I cannot say how he will be in the future, I cannot say if he will ever recover fully. I know that we will need to work in keeping our relationship strong. I know that there will be tough times and there will be happy ones, but in the end, this is what life is all about!"

"Even though we are apart for some of the year, we are still a team, and I come and see him just as often as I can. In 2018, I spent more time in the UK than in Nairobi. So I still feel that I am still just as involved in every aspect of his life and his treatment, from all his medical appointments to what he eats, and how he feels."

Gladys knows that, despite all of the hardships they have faced – and have still to face – the journey has shown their love for each other. "We are still in the process of getting to know each other again. I feel that this will be a non-ending process. We will need to work every day on our relationship, but I know it will be worth it."

"You can't ever give up on your loved one. For anyone out there, facing something like this, try to be patient and to show love… loads of love. I can tell you that there will be occasions when you just want to give up but, as an old saying has it: *when you feel like quitting think about why you started.*"

"You will learn plenty about yourself in the process. And you might surprise yourself at just how strong you are. I have learned that I can be stronger than I thought I was. I have learned that I can be resilient. I have learned that I can give support and strength to someone else and that I can make a difference. And last, but not least, I have discovered what a person can achieve if the driver is love."

Keep believing in them

Everyone involved is justifiably proud of what Ash has achieved. Gladys says, "His determination, his willingness to keep going despite all the hitches he's gone through." His progress is all the more remarkable for the fact that his family has been caring for him, without any additional support for several months.

Not everyone gets the funding they need to have the sort of ongoing care, support and rehabilitation their loved one needs. Sameera says, "That was the case for us. Although we did have some support initially, the funding ran out, and we had to make different arrangements."

"Me and my mum take it in turns, and my sister does it at the weekends, so we all help, and we all play a big part in Lali Mamu's recovery. I gave up my career for a little while, so I could help. And I know plenty of other people have to take that decision too. When you're doing this for a loved one, the biggest difficulty is keeping your professional head. Sometimes, it can be very challenging to put your family side away and remember, you are doing a job in those hours. Then you can go back to being a partner, daughter or niece after that. Sometimes you can leverage being a niece in the job too … I think I probably get away with a lot more than the carers did!"

"Of course, in Lali Mamu's eyes, I'm always going to be that child so that's the battle I have on a daily basis.

I'm seeing someone who was my father figure struggle – and it's difficult to see that. But I'm doing my best to take a professional view of it. This is my job. That's how I cope with it. And I'm used to taking professional detachment in my professional life as a solicitor, so I tap into a bit of that."

"I think you have to retain your belief in that person. You have to go on encouraging them, every day. You need to keep them feeling empowered as much as possible. So I encourage Lali to do as much as he can for himself."

"You need to stay strong, and I know that can be really hard at times. Make sure you have a support network around you, and talk about how you're feeling. That is really important. I learnt about that with my mum. There was so much I felt I couldn't talk to her about because I didn't want to upset her. But then I found out that she felt the same – she really needed to talk, and felt like she couldn't. Now, we're both able to talk about it all, we feel a lot less overwhelmed by the difficulties we sometimes face."

"I think there are lots of advantages to caring for your loved one yourself. Finding the right carer isn't always easy, for all sorts of reasons. And it means that when you have to do something difficult or stressful, you're the best person to help your loved one to do it. When I have to give him medicine, he knows that it's good for him, and he needs to have it. He trusts me."

"When I took him to Kenya, I did it as his PA. He probably wouldn't have been able to do that with a normal care package in place. But I knew he was ready and able to go, and it made sense for us to do it together. We try and get out of the city as often as we can. We get out to eat, and we go and see some Bollywood films." Ash says, "We've been out to some of the places that I used to take the girls as children, and it has been very, very nice to see them again."

Sameera's experience of caring for Ash offers hope to anyone who will be caring for a loved one. "I know it can be a scary prospect if you don't get external support, or you don't get the funding you need. It was a difficult prospect for us, and we all had to try and find ways to raise the money. The family really pulled together to help pay for the surgery he needed in Kenya."

"I know how hard it's been for Lali Mamu sometimes," Sameera says. "And I know how frustrated he gets, but he has stayed so positive – and he keeps us going as well!" My sister came in the other day saying things were tough at work, and he sat her down and said "It's alright, little one. You can do it." And my sister said, "This is the man who's still recovering from a near-death experience, and he's helping me feel better." He keeps us going. In many ways, he's even more encouraging now than ever. He's so proud of our achievements.

"And even though his life is physically more difficult and more tiring that it used to be, he doesn't allow himself to let it get him down. He doesn't have any time for negative thinking."

Whatever the future brings

Tim is really pleased with Ash's progress, "Ash made some really significant improvements, physically. And I think his enjoyment of some of the things he was doing really increased. He was at the stage too where I felt that he wasn't going to go backwards in his physical recovery – and that's a really important determinant of long-term improvement. And I think he will continue to improve.

Ash is a really great guy, and he's still got all those elements to his personality that people have always loved him for."

Perhaps Gladys is most able to see the changes in Ash. "He is basically the same person that he was before the accident, but now everything is sort of magnified. If he is happy, he is extremely happy, but he can easily get emotional and show his feelings with no boundaries. When he is frustrated or angry, those feelings are magnified as well. Sometimes I think that his brain injury has exponentially increased whatever feelings he has. He keeps reminding me that he loves me, which is a constant in our conversations. And I love that. It was the same before the accident, no day passed without him telling me how much he loved me and how important I was for him."

"I feel that the accident has made our relationship and our commitment to one another stronger and more solid. We've been through a lot in these last two years; however, our love and respect for each other has remained intact and even grown stronger."

"I have had to endure some people questioning why I would stay by Ash's side if I was not certain what the future would bring for us. I heard people telling me 'He is not the father of your children, why do you have to stay?' I am not going to lie. These two years have been extremely difficult and painful, there have been moments in which I did not know what was going to happen, but there has been always something very clear to me: I wanted, and I want, to be by Ash's side, no matter what the future brings for us."

Chapter 8

The rehab assistant

Tim Pattle

My background is in sport science, and I understand what meaningful physical activity can do to improve a person's sense of well-being. This is no different for anyone who has had a brain injury. There are immense benefits for many clients of doing activities that were important to them pre-injury, as demonstrated in my work with Ash.

I actually started out as a tennis coach, but I was talking to Katherine about the relationship between activity and sport on rehab. There are studies being done at the moment looking at the benefits of physical activity for people who have had a brain injury and people with dementia. At the time, Katherine was working with a gentleman in a care home next to a tennis centre. He was displaying aggressive behaviour in the home, and they were thinking of ways to help him channel his frustration in a more productive way.

We found out that he used to play tennis, so Katherine brought him along to the tennis centre, just to hit some tennis balls with me. Almost as soon as he got on the court, he was like a completely different person. His wife was watching, and it was really quite emotional for her. It was as if she was getting her husband back.

All of the skills that he'd learned earlier in his life – the different techniques for hitting the ball and the fine motor skills – all came back. And that really got us thinking in more detail about the possibilities of physical activity for people with brain injuries. It demonstrated the potential of community rehab – of doing meaningful things that people used to do, pre-injury – and how they can tap into the physical and cognitive part of the body and the brain to aid recovery.

So my focus is finding what meaningful physical activity we can encourage the client to do. That is determined to a large extent by their capability – what can they do? When I have found something they can – and will – enjoy doing, my approach is simple: let's go and do it (within the bounds of risk assessment). We're here to test what can be done in a safe environment.

I meet a lot of people who are told "You can't do that anymore" or "You're not allowed to do that" – but I'm more interested in what they can do. Together we will discover just what they can accomplish. This more proactive approach is usually really positive.

I usually have to work within a timeframe of twelve weeks, depending on what funding is available. Some cases can go on for long, long periods of time if we're working with severe injuries. We rely a lot on input from the family to determine what the person was like before the injury and get a sense of what they were capable of pre-injury.

However long we have, it's important that the work we do and the improvements we make are quantifiable. We use an assessment tool to record people's standards at the start of the process and again at the end. Improvements can be quite hard to quantify in some cases. In Ash's case, we looked at things like punch combinations in his work at the gym. How many times did he do it correctly? How accurate was he? The psychology, physio, rehab and occupational therapy teams all feed back into the report.

We take a very flexible approach. If things do not work, we try something else. We timetable all the activities so that there is a set structure in place. We do not want to overburden anyone, so we don't plan too many activities in one day. We try to limit physical activities to the morning, and programme in plenty of rest, so that it doesn't feel too onerous. One of the difficulties we sometimes have is pacing the work so that it feels meaningful and challenging without going too far, too fast.

It is important for us to work around the family's schedule too; we know how important it can be for them to take part and to give their support and encouragement. The involvement of the family is really important in every case, and certainly in Ash's case, his family really rallied round. I was mindful of just how scared and uncertain they were feeling too. They didn't quite know how to manage Ash's expectations for recovery, so Katherine and one of our psychology colleagues, Carol, got more involved to help them in their own right.

Families often need clear advice on how to act consistently with regard to de-escalating the situation when things got tense. Equally, they needed to know how to avoid becoming the target of their loved one's frustrations when they flare up. It is a tricky situation for any family – so much of the person is still there, but they may not be quite the same as they were before. In Ash's case, his family had to get used to the fact that the ways in which he treated them were going to be a bit different.

There will be times when we work with people whose abilities are very compromised as a result of their injuries.

In these cases, it is important to find out what their priorities are, so that we can start to work towards them. Even if we have to scale back in terms of what we can't do, there are always many other things we *can* do.

Everyone has to adjust after a significant injury – the client, family and friends – but our work shows that there is always hope for a brighter future.

Part V

In sickness and in health

Katherine Dawson

Introduction

Lisa had a stroke in November 2016 and sought therapy this year, specifically to help with managing her emotions. I met up with Lisa and her daughter in March 2020 to complete an assessment. We began by discussing the stroke Lisa had experienced, as well as the events that led up to the stroke, and how Lisa has coped since. They told me about the difficulties Lisa had conversing in group conversations and how she found it hard to follow a plot on the television. It was clear as the assessment progressed that the emotional changes and fatigue were now the most disabling effects for Lisa and her family. In terms of emotional change, Lisa talked about crying at the drop of a hat, and regularly doubting herself. There had been times – even quite recently – when she had felt as if she was going mad.

We spent some time discussing what the stroke meant to Lisa and her family. Lisa explained that she felt mad at herself because she hadn't overcome the impact of the stroke, both at work and home. She described how everyone's lives had changed as a result of her injury. And I was struck by the strong sense of guilt Lisa described.

Lisa was also dealing with a strong sense of loss of role, particularly when her family were trying to support her and remove demands from her. Prior to the brain injury, Lisa had been the organiser of the family. Her daughter explained that now, when the family express their concern that Lisa should rest, she can become a little defensive, and this can increase her levels of stress. Lisa explained that she still sees herself as a strong person but the strength of feeling inside of her can become intolerable when she can't switch her brain off.

Lisa struck me as having a great deal of insight into the changes in thinking and memory following her stroke, and she has some good strategies in place to compensate. Lisa also described a sense of determination that this stroke was not going to stop her, but was frustrated and stressed when its effects overcame her. She had a keen sense of loss regarding who she is – compared with who she was – and where she is headed.

Towards the end of the assessment, we discussed together that there are a number of layers to how Lisa was feeling:

Before the stroke, life was working okay for her – she had a job she enjoyed and was good at, and family was really important.

Post stroke, with regard to the damage to Lisa's brain, imaging had indicated an acute right temporoparietal infarction (implicating the right temporal and parietal lobes of the brain). We discussed the link between damage in that part of the brain and functions, which include the following:

- Recollection of information told to Lisa
- Working memory – holding information in very short-term memory and working something out
- Switching attention between topics

- Sustained attention when focused on a specific goal and the ability to filter out distractions in the environment

The above are hidden difficulties. Often, when it is overloaded, the brain can become agitated, which is what happened to her in the busy office environment at work, or in a conversation with too many people. In addition to this, we also discussed that Lisa was then appraising this experience in a self-critical way; she was blaming herself for no longer being able to cope, and that just led to more self-blame and distress.

Lisa described herself as being a very independent person and has successfully 'boxed' previous trauma in her life but remains frustrated that she cannot do the same with the stroke. We discussed how that might mean she is more at risk of 'boom-bust' – as she describes in her story – as pacing herself would be difficult to do consistently, given her strong need to get on with life.

At this point, we discussed specific interventions. I recommended psychological therapy with my colleague, Dr Carol Bolton, who would support Lisa to adjust with more self-compassion for her acquired brain injury and explore self-care/emotional coping strategies.

We talked about a specific goal to decide on how she would like to refer to this event in her life and what would be acceptable to think and feel.

With regard to cognitive rehab, I also thought it was important to separate out what things are a consequence of her brain injury and then find ways of compensating creatively for difficulties with attention in the workplace to help her manage her fatigue. We discussed options including the following:

- Slightly shorter days

- Longer breaks – Lisa only took 30 mins for lunch at the time of the assessment
- Use of noise-cancelling headphones, so her brain does not have to work as hard to filter out background noise in a busy office environment

Lisa subsequently began work with my colleague, Carol, who has summarised their sessions to date below:

> *We began our sessions by finding out about how Lisa has dealt with the stroke and the impact it has had upon her life. In particular, she spoke about how her role as a mother and a homemaker has changed, and how difficult she finds it now that she is no longer "the strong one for everyone else".*
>
> *She spoke about the critical voice that is always with her. In talking about this critical voice, Lisa spoke about events from her past that have led her to develop certain strategies to help her cope with what has been happening. We spoke about how these strategies were very helpful back when she was having a difficult time in the past, but now they are no longer needed. Lisa acknowledged that letting go of those strategies made her feel very vulnerable.*
>
> *We talked about how her beliefs applied to others but not herself. For example, Lisa agreed that asking for help is a strength, and said that she would like her children to be able to care for others… But she struggles to apply this kind of thinking to herself.*
>
> *In between sessions, Lisa would set herself challenges for the week, e.g. I am to be more honest when I am feeling tired or down. When doing this repeatedly, Lisa found that her mood improved, and she was able to feel more relaxed at home. She was also spending more time with her son and her husband, so she felt closer to*

them because of this. She has stopped apologising if she asks for help and she has noticed that her critical voice has been getting much quieter.

On the next page, you will find out how the stroke impacted on the lives of Lisa and her family, and how, despite the setbacks, Lisa and her husband have managed to go on loving and supporting each other…

Chapter 9

Lisa's story

Lisa Summerill

Before I has my stroke I was working full time as an accounts administrator for a small manufacturing company. I have a husband, Alan, who you'll hear from later, and two children: my son was around 15 at the time was living at home with us. My daughter was a bit older.

My grandson was born in the February, and I had the stroke in the November of 2016. Up until I had the stroke, I'd been a healthy, happy person. I didn't have any underlying health conditions that I knew of. We loved being part of our children's lives, and we looked after my grandson every weekend… But that had to stop straightaway. My life changed totally. I was just 47.

I was at work when it happened; I can remember it as if it had happened five minutes ago. I was at my desk eating lunch – I'd had my sandwich and I was trying to open a little snack-pack of grapes. And I remember very clearly thinking that my fingers felt wrong – they seemed fat and heavy. In my mind, I was thinking, *what's happening, why can't I open this packet?*

I finally managed to yank it open, and the grapes flew everywhere. I turned around, and one of my colleagues who sat two desks away looked at me and said, "Lisa, are you alright?" And as he said it, I felt as if somebody had shoved a massive electrical cable though the top of my head. And that was it. I slumped forward onto my desk.

They did the FAST Test – my face had slumped, my arm was weak and I couldn't speak, so they rang 999. As soon as the paramedics saw me, they knew I'd had a stroke. They took me to our local hospital. I was assessed straightaway, but they said I'd had a migraine. They gave me a CT scan but couldn't see anything strange on that. So they sent me home…

The next few days are just blur. I know I was going backwards and forwards to the hospital every day. There were 999 calls and ambulances, but every time they sent me home, saying I'd had a migraine. I'd suffered migraines as a child; I knew it wasn't that. I could hardly walk. My speech had gone.

I can't really remember any of it, I've just pieced it together from what my husband and my children have told me.

ALAN: Lisa had the stroke on Thursday. We went back and forth to the hospital over the next few days, but nothing was being done for her. We were sent home, and that first weekend was just shocking. She couldn't go up and down the stairs, I had to help her go to the toilet. She was out of it; she just didn't know what had happened, and we didn't get the scan and the diagnosis until Sunday…

The next vivid memory I have is four days later, on the Sunday morning, my parents came up from London and as soon as I heard my mum's voice outside, it was as if I regressed to a child. I started crying and saying "That's my mum," over and over again. It was upsetting for everyone to see.

Then my husband got a phone call from the hospital, telling him to take me back in for an MRI scan that morning. And, that is when they found the evidence of the stroke and admitted me straight onto the stroke ward. There had been a carotid artery bleed that led to the brain and then clotted on the brain.

I stayed on the ward for a week. I was given speech therapy and had to learn to walk again. Before they would release me, I had to be able to walk up and down the stairs by myself, and I had to be able to make a cup of coffee and a bowl of cereal and a slice of toast. After that, improvements happened slowly.

ALAN: At first, she couldn't even remember the alphabet. When she came home, she still couldn't walk very well, and her speech was still not very good. She didn't have a dropped face, but just looking at her, you knew something was wrong.

It was so strange, lying in the bed with her and thinking: the thing that's caused this is just a few inches from my face. Just under the hair, under the skin, and it's changed everything!

In the first few weeks and months, I had a lot of appointments with the consultant on the stroke unit, and the stroke rehabilitation team. There were lots of memory tests and other psychological evaluations. The speech therapy continued because I developed a strange cough and kept losing my voice. So as well as not being able to speak properly, I had no voice to speak with. I still suffer from that today. When I'm really tired, my speech slows down, and if I get really stressed my voice disappears altogether. There's no sore throat, no cough; it just goes.

So many little things felt impossibly difficult. I couldn't even cross a road if there was a junction; I didn't understand the way the traffic moved. My depth perception has never been the same either. I can climb the stairs in my house because I know them, but if I have to go anywhere else and use stairs, I really struggle. Even a slight change in the level of the pavement is really challenging. It feels to me as if there is a step there, and then I have to physically stop and lift my leg up as if I'm going over a step – and there's nothing there!

ALAN: She couldn't gauge how fast the traffic was coming. So I used to go out with her, and we walked to the local shop one time. Before we'd even been down one aisle, there were people stopping to talk with her, and asking how she was getting on, and in just a few minutes, you could see the difference. The effort of all that thinking and talking was so great, her speech started to slow. It was as if her battery level was going down.

The stroke hasn't left me with any physical deficits, although it left me with a lot of neuralgic pain. The medication I was on just wasn't working for me, so I had acupuncture to help me deal with that.

ALAN: We found out that a stroke doesn't normally leave you in any pain, so she was very unlucky. But it had caused a lot of nerve damage, which is why everything hurt so much. She was on paracetamol at first! But then they put her on morphine for the pain, and that really knocked her out. It took a while to get her meds balanced, and they had to try a few different things. But it went on for over a year, and we were desperate. Every time they tried a different medicine, or a

> different combination, we were hoping that would be the one. It was such a tough journey for her, trying to break through that pain barrier.

I went from being an outgoing, happy person to someone who doesn't really socialise any more. I've got a small group of friends, but I tend to stay home now, instead of going out. I do get overcome with chronic fatigue very easily, so I just don't have the energy to go out.

I don't drink anymore, so that had a knock-on effect with the socialising and going out too. Places that I might have gone to before just aren't enjoyable for me anymore. A lot of that is because of the noise – if there's too much noise going on, my brain just can't cope. It stops. It gets to a point where it can't take it in, and I get quite vacant then. If there are more than three or four people in the room, I can't join in with their conversations, so it's left me feeling quite isolated at times. I'm alright with one-to-one conversations, but even then, my brain starts to wander after a while, and I lose track of what I'm saying and what's going on in the conversation. So that's affected me too.

In March 2017, four months after the stroke, I was able to go back to working from home in the same job, doing a couple of hours here and there, until I was able to go back into the office for a few days.

It felt like a little victory getting back to work, but I felt as if I had lost some of the richness in my life. I would go to work and then come home, and that was it! We couldn't have our grandson over to stay overnight every week, because he's such a bundle of energy, and I just can't keep up with him. So we went from seeing him every week to seeing him every three weeks, and just having him for one night.

I couldn't go to the gym any more. I used to enjoy swimming, but it feels too difficult now, and I get frustrated by that. So the knock-on effect of that is that I get upset again. My mood can be quite low. I still have rough days when I feel more pain. I've got a constant headache, more of a dull, heavy sensation in the top of my head where the brain injury is. But having seen the scan and the significant scale of the injury, that's not surprising.

It was hard for all of us, of course, especially my husband, Alan. He basically went from being my husband to being my carer. Even now, he still does quite a few things for me that I used to do for myself. But for months after it happened, he had to do everything. I couldn't bathe; I couldn't even get dressed on my own. And he struggled with that transition.

Emotionally, I think it affected Alan more than it affected anyone else. The counsellor that I'd been seeing came to see Alan. And they told me that he had been traumatised by what had happened. He simply hadn't been prepared for just how impaired I was going to be.

ALAN: I know I could have had some ongoing counselling, but I didn't. At one point, I did go and see my GP and he told me I was suffering from carer's stress. So what do you do about it? I didn't want to go on antidepressants. Five years on, did I make the right decision?

I don't think it antidepressants or counselling would have worked for me, but that's not to say they won't work for you. Stick together, and carry yourselves through it as best you can, but don't be afraid to take what help works for you. There's no rulebook. In the end, we found our own ways of coping.

Alan still finds it very difficult to talk about – and I know he's not alone in that. Lots of husbands and wives must feel like they've lost a spouse and gained a caring job they never wanted or asked for. We always used to have a good connection, physically as well as mentally, but this has had an impact on our physical relationship. I find it difficult now, and that has been hard for us both to deal with. We're not old people, it shouldn't have been an issue for us. It's not easy to accept the way we live now, compared with how we used to live, and accept the compromises we have had to make.

There is a chunk of my life missing too, and it is something that I feel I need to try and understand for my own sake. I still ask Alan about the missing pieces, but I know how hard it is for him to take his mind back there. It brings up the anger again too. He's angry that things were missed; he's angry that I was told at one stage that I was 'faking it!' And it's hard to let go of that level of anger.

My daughter was at the hospital quite a lot, and she can fill in some of the gaps. And my son has only recently started to talk to me about it. He told me that when I came home from the hospital, I couldn't even recognise him. And I know how upsetting it must have been for him when I kept asking, "Who is he?"

It had a big impact on my parents and my brother too. Even now, they get upset if they see me having a bad day, particularly if my speech starts to slow, or I seem more tired than normal. As a family, we're coping better with it now than we were, but it's been frustrating for all of us. And the truth is, I *have* changed…

I am a different person now. I can be difficult. I get very anxious. I'm snappy. We're not just living with the injury, we're all living with the ongoing effects of it. And that is hardest on Alan. But he has traditional values. He won't ever go back on the vows he made to me. We stood in church and said that we would love and care for each other, 'in sickness and in health, for better, for worse, till death us do part.' So as hard as it is for him, he still wants to fulfil that role. We're still in love with each other, and we have just had to adapt.

ALAN: Everything changed, everything was different. We hadn't asked for any of what happened. But this was my wife, and I'd made her a promise when we'd got married. Lisa had always stood by me when I'd gone through tough times. It was my time to stand up and look after her, as I knew she would look after me.

It's difficult seeing the person you love in so much pain, and you can't do anything to ease their pain. In the end, you just plough on, as I imagine thousands of other partners and carers do, and you stay as positive as you can. You have to get into the mindset that you carry on as normal. You keep working, you keep bringing the money in, paying the bills, and you look after each other.

For a long time afterwards, we lived slightly separate lives. I still wanted Alan to go out and socialise with our friends. I didn't think he should be stuck in the house just because I was. And that was a struggle; he wanted to go out, but I knew he felt guilty about leaving me behind. He felt as if he was leaving me all on my own all day while he was at work, and then doing it all over again in the evenings. But I wanted him to go out; I didn't want him to suffer because of what had happened to me. Getting through that was hard, and it has taken time for us to feel like we have started to get the balance right. It all takes time.

And it isn't always easy. I miss the old me! I do still try to be as much of the person as I possibly can be, but I struggle with that sometimes. Just practically it's hard because I can't plan things. If somebody gets in touch and asks if I fancy going out the next day, or if we want to go out as a couple, it doesn't matter how much I might feel like I want to do it, I know that, if I feel really fatigued the next morning, I won't be able to. I have to say to Alan, "You go if you want to, and I'll see how I feel." Or perhaps he'll go round earlier, and I'll try to join them later. Or I'll pop in for a bit and stay for as long as I'm comfortable. Again, it's all about adapting to our new situation. But it does take a lot of work.

On the positive side, I do feel as if we spend a bit more quality-time together now. Before, we would be in the house together, but doing our individual things. We tend to do more together now; we found things that we both want to watch on TV, or music that we want to listen to. It's all about adapting.

From day one, I've said, every day's a bonus now, and we really do try to make the most of each day. Part of making that work is getting into the mindset of taking each day as it comes. On a bad day, I just have to think: *I just have to get through it as best I can, and try again tomorrow.*

It isn't always easy, but I think you have just got to be open and honest with each other. And that's been a really important learning experience for me. I've always been a 'paint a smile on my face' kind of girl, so I have had to learn that, if I wake up in the morning and I'm having a rough day, then I need to say, "Please bear with me if I'm getting a bit fractious, or if I just need to go and sleep." Before I would have tried to push my real feelings away and carry on as normal, but now I've learned how to be a bit open about it.

I think that helps, but it was hard at first, because it made me feel more vulnerable. Before that, Alan would look at me sometimes and know something was wrong, but because I wasn't honest about how I was feeling, it made us both feel awkward if I told him I was fine. And that put him in the quandary of thinking: do I keep asking her, or do I leave her alone now?

If you can be honest with your friends and family, it will help you. They won't feel like they're walking on egg shells around you, and it will be less draining for you to try and keep up a pretence.

My friends have been really supportive, even when I've had to cancel things. I often feel like I've let them down, and I'm constantly apologising for that. But I understand that it might be difficult for people who don't know me quite so well to understand why I am the way I am. Partly that's because there is no physical indication that there is anything wrong with me. If you saw me in the street, you wouldn't know I'd had a stroke. And yes – some people have said, "You don't look like you've had a stroke!" Sometimes, the better you do, the more quickly people forget. Because I've picked up where I left off at work as much as I possibly can, people forget that there are still things I can't do. Or I have to remind people why I might be feeling tired, or why noise might be affecting me. It's hard in an open plan office to have to ask people to be quiet because you're feeling sensitive to noise.

I'm not able to join in with the office banter anymore because I wouldn't be able to concentrate on my work. And when I first went back to work, it was really difficult; I didn't feel like I was a part of the team in the same way, even after working there for ten years.

One of the hardest adjustments I've had to make has been dealing with my low mood, but it's been an important work, for all of us. To begin with, I really struggled to cope with the difficult days. I wasn't used to feeling so low, so often. There are still days when I can just burst into tears for no reason. (And here are some times when I will just burst into manic laughter for no reason!) So I contacted Headway – the brain injury association – and Different Strokes – the stroke charity, and I've used their private Facebook accounts, and it was really useful to read about other people's experiences. Sometimes it just helps to know that it isn't just you; you're not a manic depressive, it's all part and parcel of having a brain injury. Other people have gone through something similar, and I could relate to so many of the experiences I read about.

Remember, you can speak to your GP, or to one of the head injury charities too. They've got telephone helplines, and they will understand what you're going through. The people on the phone lines have either had a stroke, or have family members who have had a stroke, so they're knowledgeable and understanding. And that's really important – being able to speak to someone who knows some of what you're feeling, and what you're going though is really helpful.

Keep on top of your medication too. Review it with your GP or your consultant, and make sure that it's still working in the right way for you. We had to play around with my meds for eighteen months before we really got it right. In the end, a slow-release medication really worked for me.

I still try to be as positive as I can, and it's important to know that some days will be easier than others, and you just need allow the bad days to happen. I know that I can talk to Alan, or to my mum. So I know I've got people I can turn to if I'm feeling really low. And if you are still struggling with the loss of who you used to be, I do urge you to speak to someone. I'm lucky to have the rehab team help me too. It's so helpful to speak to someone who understands why the things that are getting me down are happening, and Katherine spent some time when we first met explaining why my brain does what it does to me!

I have since started working with Carol who is a clinical psychologist, and we are focusing on developing the tools I need to help myself cope when I struggle. When you live with a condition day-to-day, it helps to have better ways of dealing with it, rather than feeling like I need to seek outside help. So I feel more able to maintain a feeling of control, and that helps me stay more positive.

I think it helps to remember that you will have plenty of ups and downs. When you're medically signed off, your journey is only just beginning. But at that point, you're told that – physically – you're okay. And that's when the people around you go back to work and back to school, and to a certain extent, life has to carry on as normal. That was a difficult stage for me. But I was of the mindset that *I have a brain injury; I'm going to have that for life*. So I know that I will need all sorts of support at different stages over the years ahead. Remember, you can turn to people at any stage in the months, or years after your stroke or head injury. Recovery is ongoing, you can always go back for help, whenever you need it. It really doesn't matter how far you've come, or how long you've gone without speaking to anyone about it.

ALAN: It was difficult when the bad times come around because we'd been getting used to being on the up. It felt like things were better; we were both at work, we were feeling more confident for the future, and then we took a nosedive.

One night, we'd ordered a takeaway, everything was good – and then, Lisa had a pain in her head, and she knew something was wrong. And that was it. Our son phoned an ambulance, and then our dinner arrived at the door, and then the ambulance arrived. It was bedlam. Thinking back on it, we're able to laugh about it, but I was terrified it was happening all over again. They kept her in overnight and diagnosed exacerbation of symptoms.

She'd been on such a high, feeling so positive, and she'd just been overdoing it. We'd been complacent. We'd forgotten what a major event we'd had.

I had a big setback a few months ago, and I was surprised that, having gone so long, on my own, I suddenly felt like I needed more help. All of a sudden, it all caught up with me and walloped me in the face. And I know that, if I hadn't had people to turn to, and if I hadn't known that there were resources and help out there for me, I really would have struggled. But I know setbacks are to be expected, and I know that I don't ever need to feel bad about it, or be hard on myself.

If things are ever really bad, I know the signs, and I will just take myself off on my own for a bit. Sometimes sleep helps, but each day is different, and I have had to learn to adapt to different feelings. Above all, I do remember how lucky I am. When the consultant did the first MRI scan, he was amazed. He told me, "Looking at this damage, it's amazing that you've survived this."

ALAN: Just look at what's happened. Look at where she's come from, and what she's achieved. She's gone back to the job she did before, doing the accounts, spending some time with her friends. We still get the ups and downs, and that boom and bust cycle is common for people who have had a stroke. But she's achieved so much.

I've never questioned, *why did this happen? Why me? What have I done?* I'm lucky that I've always been quite a determined person. I've been through so much in my life that didn't beat me, and I wasn't going to allow this to beat me either. There was only one time when I felt so bad that, just for a moment, I thought: *I've got all these tablets here, all this morphine…* The pain was too much.

But I was lucky; I knew I had support. And I've got a loving husband, two beautiful children and a grandson that I need to be here for. There's no better motivation than that!

I promise you, there is support out there for you if you need it. Never be afraid to ask. As Katherine would tell you, "It's okay not to be okay. Just try to be as honest as you can be about what you're feeling and what you're going through with the people around you."

ALAN: If there's one piece of advice I can give to help loved ones and family members cope with the situation it's this: don't bite back! Even if your partner or your friend who has had the stroke or other impairment seems like they're being unreasonable, don't try and argue with them. It does not work! Lisa's stroke affected the emotional part of the brain. It affected her quick decision-making and finer decision-making, so I had to keep than in mind.

You have to remember your lives have changed. I know it's hard, but you do have to learn to adapt to that. Sometimes, you have to take what they say with a pinch of salt. And, I have to give credit where it's due, I learnt that from my son. That's how he decided to deal with it. He'd shrug and think Mum's having a bad day, it'll level out.

Everything is going to be different. The survivor's brain has to learn how to do things differently. And that is going to take some getting used to, for both of you. Just remember the love you have for your friend or partner. Hang on. Be strong. It will get better.

You never know what the future is going to bring. We weren't expecting this, we didn't want this, but this is the avenue that came along; it could have been worse. Lisa can walk, she can speak, she can feed herself, and on her good days, you wouldn't even know it had happened. But if she hadn't been able to do those things, our lives would have been different again. And much harder. And that's why I'm not bitter, I'm grateful for what we've managed to get back.

It's alright to admit that you need help; don't be afraid to accept help when it is offered. Trust in your friends and family. They can help you get through this.

I really am so grateful that I'm still here, with my loving family, and I can look forward to more wonderful days to come.

Part VI

Surviving and thriving

Katherine Dawson

Introduction

I began working with Meg in 2014. At that time, she was living in her mum and dad's home locally, and plans were in place for a move to her own property. Meg's mood was extremely low, she experienced suicidal thoughts regularly and presented with high levels of panic and anxiety. She was fiercely independent prior to her illness, and again, this reminds me of the importance of thinking about how injury affects someone's identity, and how it makes sense for people to want to hold onto who they were after a trauma.

At the start of our work, we focused on education regarding panic and anxiety and the introduction of alternative coping strategies. We also talked a lot about her difficulties accepting help, and I think this was really important. The more it was discussed and named, the less likely it was for Meg to feel as stuck. We then had a break in therapy when I went on maternity leave, but on returning, Meg's anxiety had reduced, and she had moved into her own place.

Our work shifted and we began to focus on Meg's brain injury. Certainly, in therapy, Meg found it difficult to concentrate and plan at times. That also had an impact on her daily life, and contributed to her increasing stress, particularly in relation to managing her university studies. She also found it very hard to regulate her mood. As a result, I worked with Meg on introducing the link between some of these more subtle difficulties, resulting from her brain injury.

Meg's brain scans showed evidence of cerebellar damage (the part of the brain that plays a major role in the control and coordination of movements), which, at the time of injury, led to swelling and diffuse damage in her brain. This diffuse damage is described as microscopic, but there are specific patterns of impairment that are associated with this type of damage. Dependent on the nature of the injury, individuals can struggle with staying engaged and focused. They can find it difficult to regulate their mood, and keep a lid on their emotions. The speed at which they process information is also markedly reduced.

Whilst these difficulties are hidden, the impact can be significant. I remember working with a client who had damage in the part of the brain responsible for holding verbal information in her working memory. This meant she experienced difficulties holding onto what others were saying to her in conversation. Instead of telling them about it, she pretended she was okay, while inside, she was in a constant state of panic about what she had forgotten. It was only after I'd explained the role of the part of her brain that was damaged, that she felt able to share her experiences with others, which then reduced her shame.

In a similar way, it was important for us to consider with Meg how any disruption to the circuit in her brain, linking the back of the brain with the front of the brain can lead to subtle but very real changes in attention and planning/problem-solving. Bearing in mind what I saw clinically with Meg (and other clients with similar injuries), I felt this also contributed to her difficulties.

In my work, I think the frontal lobes of the brain are the most complex. More recent research shows that within this part of the brain, different parts perform different functions, and whilst paper and pencil (or computerised tests) are great at picking up on certain difficulties, it is only by pulling information from a number of sources that we can truly understand what is going on in someone's world. It is crucial to spend time with the person themselves in order to understand their challenges, as well as understanding who they are as a person, their life history and relationships. Linking in with family and care staff, as well as taking into account brain scans and test scores is also critical.

Once Meg had the information in front of her visually, she completely grasped the concept of her injury and saw how it impacted her mood. I felt her therapy really moved forwards at this point, and she was more open to strategies to help with planning. She really got on board with the work we did to reduce some of the tougher life-demands and helped her focus on what she herself wanted to achieve.

At the same time, it was really helpful getting a pain psychologist on board. Working alongside her physio and occupational therapist, the pain psychologist focused on Meg's expectations of managing pain and helped her develop better coping strategies. Meg also needed an opportunity to give herself space to grieve for her losses, as you'll read in her story...

Chapter 10

Meg's story

Meg Archer

I was a typical eighteen-year old. I was at college, I had a part-time job, and I partied hard. I knew how the world worked, and I knew exactly what I had to offer. I was confident, outgoing, and having a great time.

In October 2010, just a few weeks after my eighteenth birthday, I started to feel really ill. I got a chest infection first. Then on Monday 25th October, I went to A&E with some suspicious symptoms. But they checked me over and sent me home.

Four days later, I collapsed at home. The last thing I remember is texting my dad to ask him to come home and make me some tomato soup! Bless him, he came right back and made me some soup; but when he tried to hand it to me, I didn't respond. Apparently, I was just staring into space.

Dad called an ambulance, and by the time it came, I had lost consciousness and was rushed to hospital.

I don't remember any of it, I don't even remember the first man who probably saved my life: the on-call anaesthetist. I was put into the CT scanner, and dropped really low on the Glasgow Coma Scale, registering brain activity. The hospital didn't have a neurosurgery ward, but fortunately, one of the doctors said, "Intubate her now and get her to another hospital where she can get immediate neurological care."

I was put into a medically induced coma – and they intubated me (which means putting a tube into my airway), and that's probably what saved my life. I later discovered that if you lose one of six abilities, e.g. your temperature control, your breathing, your bowels and bladder, you normally die. I lost my breathing, but the intubation meant it could keep me ventilated.

My mum and her partner were in North London when they heard the news. Somehow, they beat my dad to the hospital, even though he was only travelling from a few miles away, and they were travelling something like 200 miles. To this day, they've never told me how many fines they got that day!

I had my first MRI scan on October 30. And that's when the second person who saved my life made his decision… the brain surgeon went to talk to my mum, my dad, my stepdad, my brother and sister and my partner, who were all in the family room. He told them straight – "If we operate, I don't know if she'll survive surgery, but if we don't operate now, Megan is going to die." The brain surgeon knew that even if I did survive, there was no knowing just how much of me my family were going to get back. In over thirty years, he had never seen anything quite like it.

It's the most traumatic thing that has ever happened to me, and I can't remember a thing about it! And I'm eternally grateful for that. I can't imagine how scared I would have been. My family still have their own issues just talking about that weekend.

By then, I had coned. In other words, my brain had dropped through the bottom of my skull onto my spinal cord. And, yes, that is as dangerous as it sounds … you have to get to about page ten of Google before it stops talking about coning in relation to the cause of death. I love telling medical people that I coned at home and hearing them say, "How are you even alive?!"

I was in surgery for about three hours, and they had to combine a lot of different surgeries to sort it out. They removed a chunk of bone from my skull, and I have a huge scar from my neck upwards. They basically had to wash my brain out due to all the gunk in there. A nice healthy brown is pink and pulsing ... mine was brown and not moving! They didn't know how much damage there was going to be.

I was still in a coma. I used to believe that people couldn't hear things in comas, but I now know otherwise. I have a clear memory from the recovery room after my surgery, of my mum, my dad and my boyfriend talking to me, and I can remember exactly what they said. When I told them what I'd heard them saying, they realised I must have been able to hear them.

I was brought round the next day. But they warned my mum and dad that if I freaked out when I woke, it could be a sign of extensive damage and a possible loss of memory. Understandably, everyone was very tense when I came round and then, I absolutely freaked out.

I was screaming and clutching at my breathing tube. My mum told me that I scanned the room, ignoring everyone until I saw her, and said, "Mum, Mum, I'm in so much pain..." and she couldn't do anything. So, they put me back under straightaway. And when they tried again the next day, I was very calm and chilled.

I was in the ICU for about seven weeks in total, but I don't remember very much about it. I do know that to start with, I didn't even believe I was ill... My family is fiercely loyal to each other, but we rib into each other like you wouldn't believe. And I genuinely thought this was the most extreme prank that anybody had every played on me!

In those first few days, nobody knew what was wrong with me. They had taken samples to grow in the lab, and it took several days before it was confirmed: it was meningococcal meningitis type B.

My parents were still trying to convince me I was ill, even though I could hardly feel anything. I could feel my face, but I couldn't feel anything else, and I couldn't move or talk. When I got tired, I didn't even have the ability to open my eyes. But still, I didn't believe them. So, they were in the terrible situation of knowing there was a very real possibility I could die, while I was being blasé about it all.

My parents were having a meeting with the doctors and nurses – who were all incredible – and told them that I didn't believe I was ill. So, the brain surgeon stopped the meeting and came straight to my room to tell me I had genuinely nearly died. At that stage, I didn't quite know who he was. (I still didn't recognise all of my family and friends either. I knew I was *supposed* to know them, but I didn't.)

It still didn't quite add up to me though. The brain really is incredible at coping with things that just don't compute. My getting ill, having brain surgery and ending up in hospital just didn't make any sense to me. So instead, my brain concocted a reality in which I was a new-born baby to my great-grandmother on my dad's side – a woman who had died twenty years before I was born. And, as far as I was concerned, it was April 1973. So, I wasn't worried about my illness; I was just worried they were going to cut me up as a time traveller to see what made me tick!

My worldview gradually shifted back to reality, particularly when I overheard a doctor talking to one of the nurses. For some reason, my hearing seemed to get exceptionally good over those first few weeks. I could hear the fluid moving in the back of my head. I could hear the doctors and nurses talking outside my room, and I heard the doctor tell the nurse, "Don't get too attached to that patient because we don't think she's going to make it."

That was the first time I ever really understood just how ill I was. But I was still so out of it at the time, that it didn't really register. I don't blame the doctor for saying what he did; I know why he said it. Most people in the ICU are either there for a couple of days and die or they start to get better and move on to other wards. By that point, I had been there two weeks and was going to be there for several more weeks.

There were so many horrendous things happening to me, but lots of funny things too. My little sister was doing a beauty therapy course at the time would do my nails for me while I was asleep, which I found very confusing when I woke up. And then there was the time my boyfriend washed my hair for me. Afterwards, he said I smelt like a wet dog, which prompted my friend to say, "Did you really say your dying girlfriend smells like a wet dog?!"

*

At five weeks in, my condition was described as critical, but stable. It was decided I needed to continue my spinal treatment at Pinderfields Hospital, but they only had one ventilator bed, which was already occupied… I needed to get off the ventilator.

I was sent to a hospital with a great reputation for helping people off ventilators a couple of weeks before Christmas. I still didn't know how ill I was, or have any idea about how long my journey towards recovery was going to be. I was clinging onto the hope that I'd be home for Christmas. I had it all worked out – I'd recuperate at home for a few weeks, and then be back at college, like nothing had ever happened.

I think it dawned on me on December 21. And I remember that date very well. I was in the high-dependency unit. There was another man in there who was also vented, who had acquired a spinal injury after falling while he was rock climbing. There was one nurse to two patients, so the nurse who looked after me also looked after him.

We were both trying to get off the vent at the same time, and the nurse would egg me on by telling me how well he'd done in his sessions breathing unaided before being put back on the ventilator, and then I would try to beat his time. I never even met the man, but it felt like there was still a real camaraderie and a healthy competition between us. Our families had bonded too after all their time together in the waiting rooms.

Then, on December 21, the nurse came in, and I knew something was wrong. She just looked so sad. I found out that the gentleman had got too ill, and they'd had to turn his life support off. I felt devastated. I didn't even know the man, but it had felt like we were friends. We had gone through so much together.

That was the point when I made the decision: *I need to do this. I can't go home.*

Getting off the ventilator was the hardest thing I had ever had to do. Humans are involuntary breathers, but at the start, I wasn't taking involuntary breaths. And it's terrifying when you're told "This machine is keeping you alive … and now we're going to turn it off"! They start by turning it off for five seconds, and then ten, and you keep on going up. I used to clock-watch constantly. Even by the time I was off the machine for two hours, I would watch every minute pass. My family tells me I was a nightmare!

It normally takes about six months for people to get off the vent, but I was so determined, I did it in just over half that time.

*

I got some movement back very slowly. Two days before Christmas 2010, my dad saw my foot twitch. Just a tiny twitch. But the fact that it was in my foot meant that the nerves all the way down my leg were working which was incredible. And after that, I could start to turn my head a little bit too.

The first time I went outside after getting ill was in a wheelchair, on a miserable day in early January. It was cold and, I could feel the rain running down my face. But I was absolutely over the moon, just to be outside again.

*

I went to Pinderfields in January 2011 and stayed there for about five and a half months. I even met the person who had been blocking the bed before Christmas, and he'd had meningitis too. I met lots of lovely people, and weirdly, it was a very happy place. We were all there for really horrendous reasons, but everyone was improving and getting better.

Being at Pinders was all about the physio. I went from hardly being able to twitch my fingers and toes to being able to raise my arms. But it was during that time that I realised I was probably never going to be able to go back to my old life. And that was hard to accept. I had been a very headstrong eighteen-year-old. I'd been working part time. I'd been doing a technical theatre course at college. And I'd been thinking about doing drama therapy with kids who had Down's syndrome and learning difficulties.

It had felt like I knew exactly what I was doing with my life, and then, out of the blue, I got ill.

I found out later that there'd been an outbreak of meningitis in York. Lots of kids got it. Some even died. Lots of university students were affected too. And one of my tutors had actually been teaching one of the kids who'd passed away.

Back then, I still thought meningitis was a bad cold that babies got. But here I am, nine years later, still recovering from meningitis. And now I know how debilitating it can be; it can take twenty years for you to recover!

*

Going back to my mum was hard. I felt like I never really came home in the way I wanted to. I couldn't get upstairs, so I had to stay in the old 1970s-style conservatory at the back of the house. None of the equipment I needed could fit in the house, and I basically lived in one room. That was nobody's fault, but it was hard.

I went from the very active person I had been, the person who said goodbye to Mum on a Friday evening adding, "Oh, I'm off to London for the weekend, I'll see you on Monday" to someone who had panic attacks just thinking about getting up and going to another part of the house. Leaving the house altogether was my worst nightmare. I was becoming agoraphobic.

I couldn't do what I wanted to do. I'd have dreams about just walking upstairs to my old room. In the end, we had to convert the conservatory into a 'granny flat' for me – and I hated calling it that! My partner moved in with me, but after three months, we broke up. We'd gone from being a really happy couple to my brain exploding and me nearly dying, and our relationship dynamics completely changed. I'm incredibly grateful to him. Even when he had every opportunity not to, he stuck around when I got ill and stayed with me for a long time afterwards.

I had a proper room that was just mine, and a bathroom in the granny flat, but I still felt like I didn't fit. So, we started house-hunting, and that's when we discovered something else…

Stepping over the threshold of a house we'd gone to look at – just a little lip of a step – I had a full breakdown. I had an overwhelming sense that I was going to trip and fall. But it wasn't a 'normal' sense of mild discomfort; I was crying and screaming. I simply couldn't cope.

My case manager referred me to speak to somebody about it, and I was diagnosed with post-traumatic stress disorder (PTSD). That explained a lot about the agoraphobia, and the night terrors I was having. I had also developed a strange sense of unease and discomfort about feeling like I had something on my face, probably related to the breathing tube, which had flopped around my face when I was vented.

I didn't know you could get PTSD from being in hospital. My therapist told me I had the same level of PTSD as another client who had watched his best friend being blown up by an explosive. I had therapy in 2013, and it changed so much for me. Although there was a lot of hard work do first …

Since getting out of the hospital, I had really only been existing – and I know that is a sad word to use for my quality of life. But that is literally what it was: sleep, wake up, have a panic attack, try to get back to sleep, wake up, panic attack … that was my existence, in my box room, in my granny flat.

There were some very dark moments. There were suicide attempts …

I hadn't even been able to let anyone help me because I didn't know what was wrong. It was horrendous. But with a change of meds, and the therapy, I went from having maybe five panic attacks a day to maybe five a week. And now, I barely have any at all.

Moving into my new house in 2017 was one of the best things I did; I love it here. The house is set up for me and all my equipment fits. This is my space. I have an incredible care team, and there is always someone here to help me. It gives me back my independence.

*

One of the hardest things I have had to deal with is knowing what might have been ... I collapsed on the Friday. But I had gone to the hospital with meningitis symptoms on Monday. Later, a consultant told me that if I had received antibiotics as late as Thursday, I would have made a full recovery. Just a standard course of antibiotics would have changed everything…

That's a lot to take in.

But frankly, I think that, in recent years, my life has been pretty amazing. I do not want a pity party. That is not why I'm telling you this story. I'm telling it because, genuinely, my life is great. Yes, I have a brain injury, and the effects will stay with me for the rest of my life, but I'm starting an OU course in 2020. I go away all the time, and I still enjoy all of my hobbies. I do embroidery, and table-top role-playing game every week. I have an incredible relationship with all of my family. I was at my sister's wedding this year, and my mum's wedding last year – to the same guy she was with when I got ill – and that was amazing.

I think everyone can agree that getting ill was not a good thing! But I am not miserable about it. Every year, I have the same conversation with my mum around the time of year I got ill. Mum is still very angry, and my parents both carry a lot of guilt about me getting ill.

They feel as if they should have been able to do something, or they should have known, and my response to that is "I'm sorry, when did you both get medical degrees?"

Mum asks me, "How are you not angry?" And I say, "Because if I let myself feel angry about it, I will never stop being angry about it. And I'm not Bruce Banner – always on the verge of turning into the Hulk!"

I'd be lying if I said that life with a brain injury is never difficult. But it doesn't have to be difficult all the time. It might sound bizarre, but I am in a really good place. I do know that it isn't like that for some people. I know I am lucky to have a wonderful home, a wonderful care team, and a wonderful family. My injury and my illness are well managed. So I genuinely believe I have been lucky: I do have some issues: my concentration still isn't great, and I am easily distracted. Fatigue is a huge issue too. But I am a high-functioning brain injury. My health is stable. And I am happy.

I think that I am essentially the same person I was before I got ill. I'm more introverted than I used to be, but I have so many wonderful people helping me, and it's no exaggeration to say that Katherine changed my life. We've been working together on and off for five years now, and I feel like she knows me like a book. She understands that I go through periods of good mental health, interrupted by dips and talking through those feelings with her makes a real difference.

Therapy is hard; it has to be hard, otherwise it won't really do anything useful. But it is so helpful. Having someone who is removed from the situation who understands me is really nice. And sometimes, it just helps to have someone to listen.

I also work with a psychologist who helps me manage pain. I've done a lot of mindfulness therapy, and I know it sounds like hippie BS, but it is actually amazingly helpful. If you're in any doubt about its effectiveness, I'd urge you to give it a try.

Working through your issues isn't just important for your recovery, I think it broadens your outlook… It is a huge thing for me to be able to say: "I have a brain injury, but my life is good." And that's what my story and this book is all about.

It took me a lot of hard work and self-reflection to get to this point. There was a slow realisation, but I think that the biggest shift in my mindset, from lamenting what I'd lost, to thinking *I'm good with what I've got* came around the end of 2017. It was when I realised that I'm probably never going to walk again. Up to that point, I was so fixated on the idea that my life would only improve when I started to walk. My mindset was stuck on: *I am putting everything else off until I can walk.* But while I was fixated on the walking, I was ignoring fifty other things that could have helped make my life amazing.

My legs do move, but I can't stand up. I don't have great sensation around my body, and I can't self-propel my wheelchair. That means I live with the idea that I may never walk again. Yes, it's frustrating when being in a wheelchair stops me doing something that I wanted to do, but there are so many other things that I love; so many other things that I still do. I don't need to be able to walk to read a really good book. I don't need to be able to walk to go and enjoy a play. It is all about focusing on the right things. There are so many things that make my life amazing, wonderful and enjoyable, that have nothing to do with being able to walk and nothing to do with my health.

I know now that you can still love things without having to put them off because you are sticking to an idea of what life *should* be like. It was a long road to really embracing that idea, but Katherine and the PTSD therapy helped me get to that point.

Age has helped too. I'm twenty-seven now. In the period of time since my illness, my grandmother passed away. I remember going to see her when she was dying. She didn't have long left, and she turned to me and said, "The worst thing that has ever happened to me is you getting ill." And I thought if the worst thing that's happened to her is what happened to me then there's more to this than being sad that my legs don't work.

I realised that getting better isn't just about recovering from being ill, it's about coming to terms with something bigger. There was a death, of sorts. My mum talks about how I was on one branch of a tree, and then I got ill and that changed things. But it doesn't mean that the tree stops growing. It's just going to grow a different branch and take a different route – and that's what I've done.

Nothing in life is set. I don't believe in fate. I didn't do anything to deserve getting ill, but the microbes and bacteria don't care. Things just happen; the universe is chaotic. So what does it matter that I can't do the things I wanted to do when I was eighteen? There's probably a very good chance that, if I hadn't got ill, I wouldn't have wanted to do some of those things anyway. You're a very different person at twenty-seven.

And I am looking ahead now…

I'm going to study for a PhD in psychology with a bit of sociology. I'll be focusing on disability, gender and death studies – and looking at how the three interact. And I know I will have as long as I want to finish my course. Then, I want to go into research. That's my long-term goal.

I hadn't realised this, but it is so easy to study now if you have a disability. And that has really opened my eyes to the possibilities out there. I was at university for a while after my illness, and they couldn't do enough for me. At the time of writing, in 2019, there is no reason why a disability should prevent you doing what you want to do. And if someone says otherwise, they are wrong. You can do whatever you want.

*

I am not going to lie, recovery takes time. It is a long, hard road. But it *does* get better. Maybe things won't go back to the way they were before the injury or illness, but that doesn't mean life isn't going to be as good. Or even better. It doesn't mean that your life can't still be extraordinary.

Remember: you have survived this. The number of people who don't survive these things is significantly higher than the ones who do survive. And you're one of those people. A genuine survivor. And that is extraordinary, and it is worth holding onto.

I had to learn to stop thinking about what I had lost, and feeling sorry about all the things I wanted that I couldn't have. I had to accept that I wasn't going to get those things.

You might wonder what would have happened if you hadn't had an accident, or hadn't fallen ill, but the fact is, no one knows… your life could have stayed on the same path and you could have wound up feeling more miserable, more unsatisfied, or even further away from the life you thought you wanted.

It's not as if, having been dealt these cards in life, we can ask for new ones. We all just have to learn to make something amazing out of the cards we've got. And I know it is entirely possible for anyone to do that. You might not be able to do it on your own; I am eternally grateful to all the people who still help and support me. But you can be (and do) amazing things. You might just be the best version of yourself, and the fact that you have an injury doesn't alter that.

I don't think I would have been able to think in this way if I hadn't been on this journey. And I am grateful for the maturity and insight it has given me. At eighteen, I thought I knew everything, I thought I was the best version of myself that I was ever going to be. But really? I was selfish, and I didn't really understand how the world worked.

Do I wish I had never got ill?

Absolutely. But I wouldn't want to go back to how I was at eighteen. I value the things I understand now because of the experience I have had. I am acutely aware of discrimination against people with disabilities and understand that life for those people can be really difficult. But I also know that when we all understand this, then we can make life better and easier for everyone.

When I was ill, I felt like I had nothing to offer anymore. But, in the years since, I have never met anyone with a disability that didn't have something to offer to society. It just took a lot of time for me to be able to think: *I have a unique experience of life. I have a lot to offer.*

Your lived experience is so important. Your voice is so important. Even if it doesn't always feel like it, you have so much to offer.

Afterword

Katherine Dawson

Having read Meg's story, I hope her message will resonate with other people who have been through life-changing trauma. I agree with Meg that she turned a corner when she began to let go of her previous life, grieve for the loss and then begin to carve out a different future. This is by no means straightforward and it can be particularly frightening when people have no sense of what the future holds when their identity has been shattered.

In order to help, I think individuals need to

- Understand what has happened to them, as I believe this strongly reduces the level of shame
- Understand their strengths and weaknesses (and for others around them to understand what they can and can't do as a result of their brain injury)
- Be given the tools to cope with their new situation, and go on to identify new goals which are meaningful

Our clients are no different to anyone else. They all want to live with meaning and have a connection with others. Whilst there are undoubtedly many barriers following brain injury, I think anyone who works in neuro rehab would agree: there are always opportunities to reduce these barriers. That is why, I think work needs to focus on helping clients regain a sense of purpose and a defined role, to bring them from vulnerability to a place of security and to help them develop their own ways of coping.

I think this takes me full circle to the conversations Karl, and I used to have about hope and the concept of slowly beginning to trust in a future, despite not knowing what that future was going to look like.

I want to end by thanking Karl, Ash and his family, Lisa and Meg, for telling their stories and highlighting the resilience that individuals show when faced with real pain and exemplifying the ability to adapt and move forwards.

Wherever you or your family are in your own journeys, I hope these stories have helped in some way. Thanks to the experiences of Karl, Ash, Lisa, Meg and many others, I strongly believe that it is possible, in time, to find meaning, opportunities and new horizons to work towards.

Rehab teams involved with Karl, Ash, Lisa and Meg

Karl

Anne-Marie Burnett, Case Manager: www.headsmartrehab.co.uk
Nicola Hunt, Clinical Specialist Physiotherapist: www.physiocarerehab.co.uk
Louise Watkins, Specialist Occupational Therapist: www.rehabilitatetherapy.co.uk

Ash

Sphere rehab team (provision of neuropsychology, clinical psychology and community rehab assistants): www.sphere-rehab.co.uk
Motion rehab team (neurological rehab company – provision of neurophysiotherapists involved with Ash's rehab) : www.motionrehab.co.uk

Lisa

Sphere rehab team: Dr Katherine Dawson, Clinical Neuropsychologist and Dr Carol Bolton, Clinical Psychologist

Meg

Dr Lisa Keegan, Clinical Psychologist:
lisa.keegan@smallsteps2wellbeing.co.uk
Vicky Draper, Chartered Physiotherapist:
https://www.csp.org.uk/public-patient/find-physiotherapist/physio2u
Julie Meighan, Specialist Occupational Therapist:
www.juliemeighantherapy.com

Bibliography

Aloni, R. & Katz, S. (2003). *Sexual Difficulties After Traumatic Brain Injury And Ways To Deal With It*. Charles C Thomas Publisher, Ltd. Springfield, Illinois.

Doidge, N. (2007). *The Brain That Changes Itself. Stories of Personal Triumph from the Frontiers of Brain Science*. Penguin Books, London.

Easton, A. (2016). *Life After Encephalitis. A Narrative Approach. After Brain Injury: Survivor Stories*. Routledge, London.

Gilbert, P. (2013). *The Compassionate Mind*. Robinson, London.

Greenburger, D. & Padesky, C.A. (2016). *Mind Over Mood, Second Edition: Change How You Feel by Changing the Way You Think*. The Guilford Press, New York.

Halligan, P.W., Kischka, U. & Marshall, J.C. (2003). *Handbook of Clinical Neuropsychology*. Oxford University Press, Oxford.

Herbert, C. & Wetmore, A. (2008). *Overcoming Traumatic Stress. A Self-Help Guide Using Cognitive Behavioural Techniques*. Robinson, London.

Hinrichsen, G.A. & Clougherty, K.F. (2006). *Interpersonal Psychotherapy for Depressed Older Adults*. American Psychological Association, Washington.

Iddon, J. & Williams, H. (2005). *Memory Boosters. 10 Steps to a Powerful Memory*. Octopus Publishing Group Ltd, London.

Irons, C. & Beaumont, E. (2017). *The Compassionate Mind Workbook. A Step-by-Step Guide to Developing Your Compassionate Self*. Robinson, London.

Judd, T. (1999). *Neuropsychotherapy and Community Integration. Brain Illness, Emotions and Behaviour.* Kluwer Academic/Plenum Publishers, New York.

Judd, T. (2003). Rehabilitation of the emotional problems of brain disorders in developing countries. *Neuropsychological Rehabilitation*, 13: 1, 307–325.

Oddy, M. & Worthington, A. (2009). *The Rehabilitation of Executive Disorders. A Guide to Theory and Practice.* Oxford University Press, Oxford.

O'Neill, H. (2009). *Managing Anger. Second Edition.* John Wiley & Sons, Ltd. West Sussex.

Powell, T. (2015). *The Brain Injury Workbook. Exercises for Cognitive Rehabilitation. Second Edition.* Speechmark Publishing Ltd. London.

Swanson, K.L. (2003). *I'Ll Carry the Fork! Recovering a Life after Brain Injury.* Rising Star Press, California.

Wilson, B.A., Winegardner, J. & Ashworth, F. (2014). *Life After Brain Injury: Survivors' Stories.* Psychology Press, London.

Wilson, B.A., Winegardner, J., Van Heugten, C.M. & Ownsworth, T. (2017). *Neuropsychological Handbook. The International Handbook.* Routledge, New York.

Winson, R., Wilson, B.A. & Bateman, A. (2017). *The Brain Injury Rehabilitation Workbook.* The Guilford Press, London.

Wood, R.L. & McMillan, T.M. (2001). *Neurobehavioural Disability and Social Handicap Following Traumatic Brain Injury.* Psychology Press, East Sussex.

Worden, J.W. (2010). *Grief Counselling and Grief Therapy. Fourth Edition.* A Handbook for the Mental Health Practitioner. Routledge, East Sussex.

Index

Note: Numbers in *italics* indicate figures in the text.